TH
OXFORD
PICTORIAL
DICTIC

Science and Medicine

THE
OXFORD–DUDEN
PICTORIAL ENGLISH
DICTIONARY

Science and Medicine

Oxford   New York

OXFORD UNIVERSITY PRESS

Oxford University Press, Walton Street, Oxford OX2 6DP

Oxford New York Toronto
Delhi Bombay Calcutta Madras Karachi
Petaling Jaya Singapore Hong Kong Tokyo
Nairobi Dar es Salaam Cape Town
Melbourne Auckland

and associated companies in
Berlin Ibadan

Oxford is a trade mark of Oxford University Press

Published in the United States by Oxford University Press, New York

Illustrations © Bibliographisches Institut, Mannheim 1979
Text © Oxford University Press 1981

The Oxford–Duden Pictorial English Dictionary first published 1981
First issued as a paperback 1984
This edition, under the title The Oxford–Duden Pictorial
English Dictionary: Science and Medicine, 1986
Reprinted 1990, 1992

Edited by John Pheby, Oxford, with the assistance of
Ronald Breitsprecher, Michael Clark, Judith Cunningham,
Derek Jordan, and Werner Scholze-Stubenrecht
Illustrations by Jochen Schmidt, Mannheim

British Library Cataloguing in Publication Data
The Oxford–Duden pictorial English
dictionary.—(Oxford paperback reference)
Science and medicine
1. Vocabulary—Pictorial works
428.1   PE1449
ISBN 0–19–281981–X

Printed in Hong Kong

Foreword

This pictorial dictionary is based on the Oxford–Duden Pictorial German-English Dictionary published in 1980. It was produced by the German Section of the Oxford University Press Dictionary Department in cooperation with the Dudenredaktion of the Bibliographisches Institut, Mannheim, and with the assistance of various British companies, institutions, and specialists. Numerous modifications of the text and illustrations of the original work have been carried out, especially regarding the depiction of everyday objects and situations, in order to allow greater scope for the treatment of these objects and situations in the context of English-speaking countries.

There are certain kinds of information which can be conveyed more readily and clearly by pictures than by definitions and explanations alone: an illustration will help the reader to visualize the object denoted by the word and to form an impression of the way in which objects function in their own technical field or in the everyday life of English-speaking countries. The layout of the illustrations and the text will be particularly useful to the learner. Each double page of the dictionary contains a list of the vocabulary of a subject together with a picture illustrating this vocabulary. This arrangement, and the presence of an alphabetical index, allows the book to be used in two ways: either as a key to the vocabulary of a subject or as an alphabetical dictionary in which the reader is referred to the section or sections in which the word is illustrated.

J.P.

Abbreviations

Am.	*American usage*
c.	*castrated (animal)*
coll.	*colloquial*
f.	*female (animal)*
form.	*formerly*
joc.	*jocular*
m.	*male (animal)*
poet.	*poetic*
sg.	*singular*
sim.	*similar*
y.	*young (animal)*

Contents

The arabic numerals are the numbers of the pictures

THE
OXFORD–DUDEN
PICTORIAL ENGLISH
DICTIONARY

Science and Medicine

1 Atom I

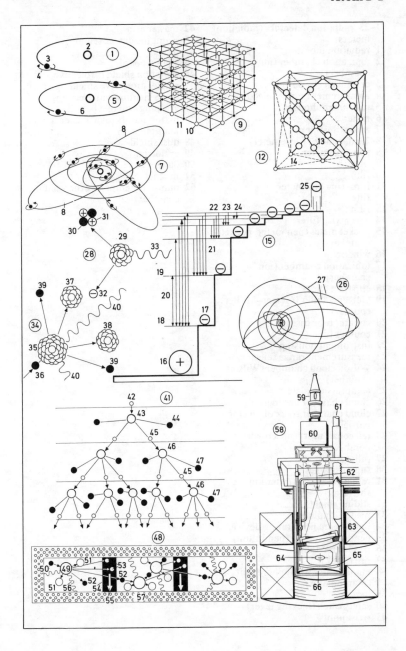

2 Atom II

1-23 **radiation detectors** (radiation meters)
1 radiation monitor
2 ionization chamber (ion chamber)
3 central electrode
4 measurement range selector
5 instrument housing
6 meter
7 zero adjustment
8-23 dosimeter (dosemeter)
8 film dosimeter
9 filter
10 film
11 film–ring dosimeter
12 filter
13 film
14 cover with filter
15 pocket meter (pen meter, pocket chamber)
16 window
17 ionization chamber (ion chamber)
18 clip (pen clip)
19 Geiger counter (Geiger–Müller counter)
20 counter tube casing
21 counter tube
22 instrument housing
23 measurement range selector
24 Wilson cloud chamber (Wilson chamber)
25 compression plate
26 cloud chamber photograph
27 cloud chamber track of an alpha particle
28 **telecobalt unit** (*coll.* cobalt bomb)
29 pillar stand
30 support cables
31 radiation shield (radiation shielding)
32 sliding shield
33 bladed diaphragm
34 light–beam positioning device
35 pendulum device (pendulum)
36 irradiation table
37 rail (track)
38 **manipulator with sphere unit** (manipulator)
39 handle
40 safety catch (locking lever)
41 wrist joint
42 master arm
43 clamping device (clamp)
44 tongs
45 slotted board
46 radiation shield (protective shield, protective shielding), a lead shielding wall [section]
47 grasping arm of a pair of manipulators (of a master/slave manipulator)
48 dust shield
49 **cyclotron**
50 danger zone
51 magnet
52 pumps for emptying the vacuum chamber

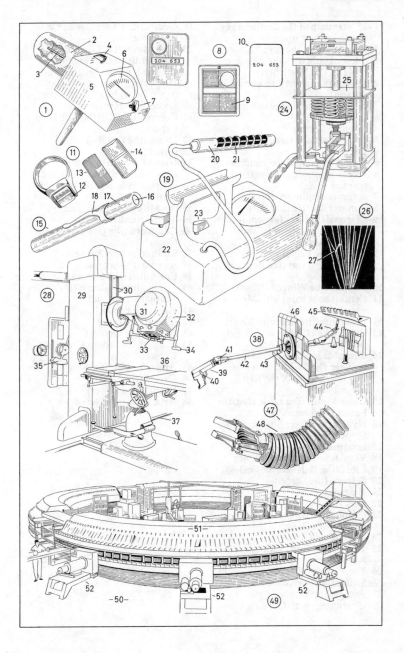

3 Astronomy I

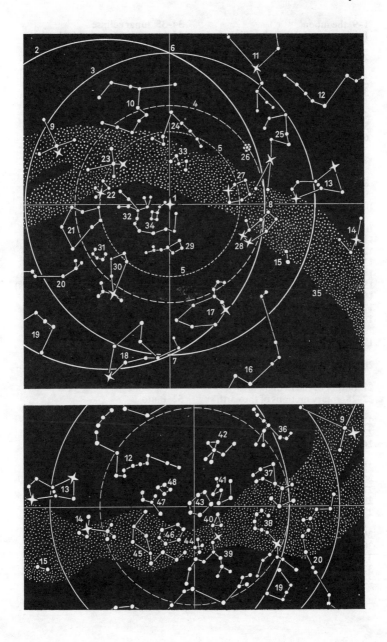

4 Astronomy II

1–9 the moon
1 moon's path (moon's orbit round the earth)
2–7 lunar phases (moon's phases, lunation)
2 new moon
3 crescent (crescent moon, waxing moon)
4 half-moon (first quarter)
5 full moon
6 half-moon (last quarter, third quarter)
7 crescent (crescent moon, waning moon)
8 the earth (terrestrial globe)
9 direction of the sun's rays
10–21 apparent path of the sun at the beginning of the seasons
10 celestial axis
11 zenith
12 horizontal plane
13 nadir
14 east point
15 west point
16 north point
17 south point
18 apparent path of the sun on 21 December
19 apparent path of the sun on 21 March and 23 September
20 apparent path of the sun on 21 June
21 border of the twilight area
22–28 rotary motions of the earth's axis
22 axis of the ecliptic
23 celestial sphere
24 path of the celestial pole (precession and nutation)
25 instantaneous axis of rotation
26 celestial pole
27 mean axis of rotation
28 polhode
29–35 solar and lunar eclipse [not to scale]
29 the sun
30 the earth
31 the moon
32 solar eclipse
33 area of the earth in which the eclipse appears total

34–35 lunar eclipse
34 penumbra (partial shadow)
35 umbra (total shadow)
36–41 the sun
36 solar disc (disk) (solar globe, solar sphere)
37 sunspots
38 cyclones in the area of sunspots
39 corona (solar corona), observable during total solar eclipse or by means of special instruments
40 prominences (solar prominences)
41 moon's limb during a total solar eclipse
42–52 planets (planetary system, solar system) [not to scale] and planet symbols
42 the sun
43 Mercury
44 Venus
45 Earth, with the moon, a satellite
46 Mars, with two moons (satellites)
47 asteroids (minor planets)
48 Jupiter, with 14 moons (satellites)
49 Saturn, with 10 moons (satellites)
50 Uranus, with five moons (satellites)
51 Neptune, with two moons (satellites)
52 Pluto
53–64 signs of the zodiac (zodiacal signs)
53 Aries (the Ram)
54 Taurus (the Bull)
55 Gemini (the Twins)
56 Cancer (the Crab)
57 Leo (the Lion)
58 Virgo (the Virgin)
59 Libra (the Balance, the Scales)
60 Scorpio (the Scorpion)
61 Sagittarius (the Archer)
62 Capricorn (the Goat, the Sea Goat)
63 Aquarius (the Water Carrier, the Water Bearer)
64 Pisces (the Fish)

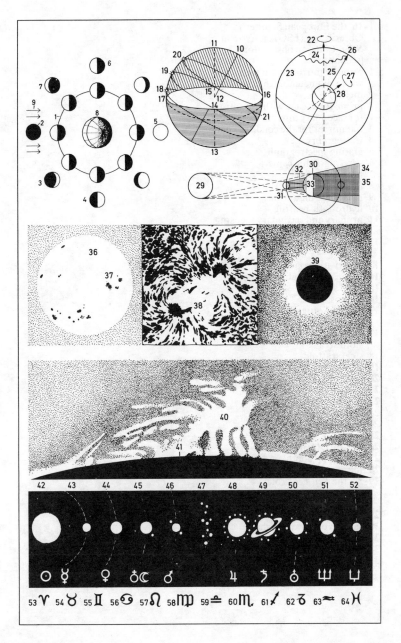

5 Astronomy III

1–16 the European Southern
Observatory (ESO) on *Cerro la
Silla, Chile*, an observatory
[section]
1 primary mirror (main mirror)
with a diameter of 3.6 m (144
inches)
2 prime focus cage with mounting
for secondary mirrors
3 flat mirror for the coudé ray path
4 Cassegrain cage
5 grating spectrograph
6 spectrographic camera
7 hour axis drive
8 hour axis
9 horseshoe mounting
10 hydrostatic bearing
11 primary and secondary focusing
devices
12 observatory dome (revolving
dome)
13 observation opening
14 vertically movable dome shutter
15 wind screen
16 siderostat
17–28 the *Stuttgart* Planetarium
[section]
17 administration, workshop, and
store area
18 steel scaffold
19 glass pyramid
20 revolving arched ladder
21 projection dome
22 light stop
23 planetarium projector
24 well
25 foyer
26 theatre (*Am.* theater)
27 projection booth
28 foundation pile
29–33 the *Kitt Peak* solar
observatory near *Tucson, Ariz.*
[section]
29 heliostat
30 sunken observation shaft
31 water–cooled windshield
32 concave mirror
33 observation room housing the
spectrograph

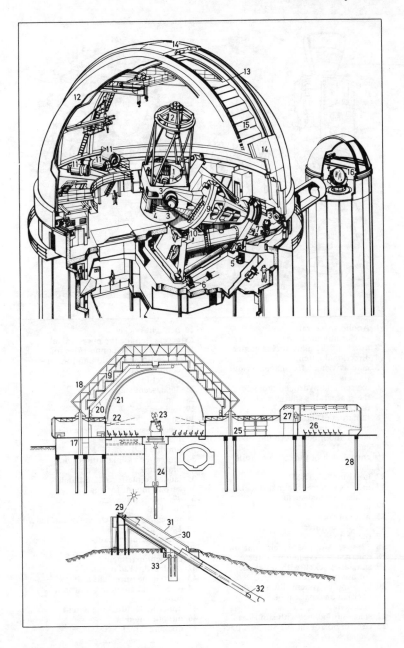

6 Moon Landing

1 Apollo spacecraft
2 service module (SM)
3 nozzle of the main rocket engine
4 directional antenna
5 manoeuvring (*Am.* maneuvering) rockets
6 oxygen and hydrogen tanks for the spacecraft's energy system
7 fuel tank
8 radiators of the spacecraft's energy system
9 command module (Apollo space capsule)
10 entry hatch of the space capsule
11 astronaut
12 lunar module (LM)
13 moon's surface (lunar surface), a dust-covered surface
14 lunar dust
15 piece of rock
16 meteorite crater
17 the earth
18-27 space suit (extra-vehicular suit)
18 emergency oxygen apparatus
19 sunglass pocket [with sunglasses for use on board]
20 life support system (life support pack), a backpack unit
21 access flap
22 space suit helmet with sun filters
23 control box of the life support pack

24 penlight pocket
25 access flap for the purge valve
26 tube and cable connections for the radio, ventilation, and water-cooling systems
27 pocket for pens, tools, etc.
28-36 descent stage
28 connector
29 fuel tank
30 engine
31 mechanism for unfolding the legs
32 main shock absorber
33 landing pad
34 ingress/egress platform (hatch platform)
35 ladder to platform and hatch
36 cardan mount for engine
37-47 ascent stage
37 fuel tank
38 ingress/egress hatch (entry/exit hatch)
39 LM manoeuvring (*Am.* maneuvering) rockets
40 window
41 crew compartment
42 rendezvous radar antenna
43 inertial measurement unit
44 directional antenna for ground control
45 upper hatch (docking hatch)
46 inflight antenna
47 docking target recess

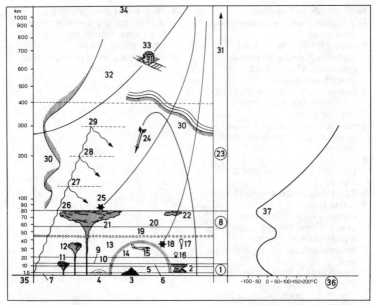

1 **the troposphere**
2 thunderclouds
3 the highest mountain, *Mount Everest* [8,882m]
4 rainbow
5 jet stream level
6 zero level (inversion of vertical air movement)
7 ground layer (surface boundary layer)
8 **the stratosphere**
9 tropopause
10 separating layer (layer of weaker air movement)
11 atomic explosion
12 hydrogen bomb explosion
13 ozone layer
14 range of sound wave propagation
15 stratosphere aircraft
16 manned balloon
17 sounding balloon
18 meteor
19 upper limit of ozone layer
20 zero level
21 eruption of Krakatoa

22 luminous clouds (noctilucent clouds)
23 **the ionosphere**
24 range of research rockets
25 shooting star
26 short wave (high frequency)
27 E-layer (Heaviside–Kennelly Layer)
28 F_1-layer
29 F_2-layer
30 aurora (polar light)
31 **the exosphere**
32 atom layer
33 range of satellite sounding
34 fringe region
35 altitude scale
36 temperature scale (thermometric scale)
37 temperature graph

8 Meteorology I

1–19 clouds and weather
1–4 clouds found in homogeneous air masses
1 cumulus (woolpack cloud, cumulus humilis, fair–weather cumulus), a heap cloud (flat-based heap cloud)
2 cumulus congestus, a heap cloud with more marked vertical development
3 stratocumulus, a layer cloud (sheet cloud) arranged in heavy masses
4 stratus (high fog), a thick, uniform layer cloud (sheet cloud)
5–12 clouds found at warm fronts
5 warm front
6 cirrus, a high to very high ice-crystal cloud, thin and assuming a wide variety of forms
7 cirrostratus, an ice-crystal cloud veil
8 altostratus, a layer cloud (sheet cloud) of medium height
9 altostratus praecipitans, a layer cloud (sheet cloud) with precipitation in its upper parts
10 nimbostratus, a rain cloud, a layer cloud (sheet cloud) of very large vertical extent which produces precipitation (rain or snow)
11 fractostratus, a ragged cloud occurring beneath nimbostratus
12 fractocumulus, a ragged cloud like 11 but with billowing shapes
13–17 clouds at cold fronts
13 cold front
14 cirrocumulus, thin fleecy cloud in the form of globular masses; *covering the sky:* mackerel sky
15 altocumulus, a cloud in the form of large globular masses
16 altocumulus castellanus and altocumulus floccus, species of 15
17 cumulonimbus, a heap cloud of very large vertical extent, to be classified under 1–4 in the case of tropical storms

18–19 types of precipitation
18 steady rain or snow covering a large area, precipitation of uniform intensity
19 shower, scattered precipitation

black arrow = cold air   white arrow = warm air

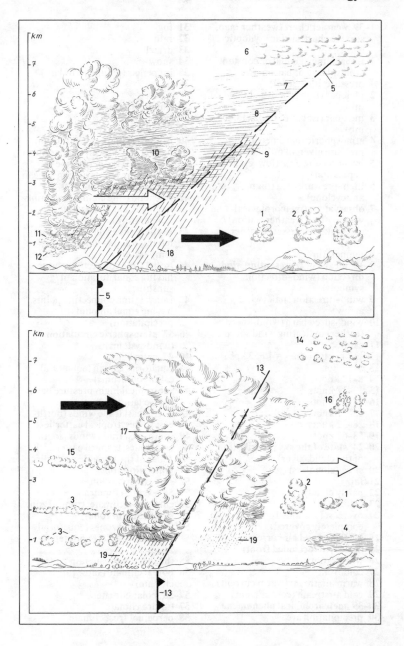

9 Meteorology II and Climatology

1-39 **weather chart** (weather map, surface chart, surface synoptic chart)
1 isobar (line of equal or constant atmospheric or barometric pressure at sea level)
2 pleiobar (isobar of over 1,000 mb)
3 meiobar (isobar of under 1,000 mb)
4 atmospheric (barometric) pressure given in millibars
5 low-pressure area (low, cyclone, depression)
6 high-pressure area (high, anticyclone)
7 observatory (meteorological watch office, weather station) or ocean station vessel (weather ship)
8 temperature
9-19 **means of representing wind direction** (wind-direction symbols)
9 wind-direction shaft (wind arrow)
10 wind-speed barb (wind-speed feather) indicating wind speed
11 calm
12 1-2 knots (1 knot = 1.852 kph)
13 3-7 knots
14 8-12 knots
15 13-17 knots
16 18-22 knots
17 23-27 knots
18 28-32 knots
19 58-62 knots
20-24 **state of the sky** (distribution of the cloud cover)
20 clear (cloudless)
21 fair
22 partly cloudy
23 cloudy
24 overcast (sky mostly or completely covered)
25-29 **fronts and air currents**
25 occlusion (occluded front)
26 warm front
27 cold front
28 warm airstream (warm current)
29 cold airstream (cold current)
30-39 **meteorological phenomena**
30 precipitation area

31 fog
32 rain
33 drizzle
34 snow
35 ice pellets (graupel, soft hail)
36 hail
37 shower
38 thunderstorm
39 lightning
40-58 **climatic map**
40 isotherm (line connecting points having equal mean temperature)
41 0 °C (zero) isotherm (line connecting points having a mean annual temperature of 0 °C)
42 isocheim (line connecting points having equal mean winter temperature)
43 isothere (line connecting points having equal mean summer temperature)
44 isohel (line connecting points having equal duration of sunshine)
45 isohyet (line connecting points having equal amounts of precipitation)
46-52 **atmospheric circulation** (wind systems)
46-47 calm belts
46 equatorial trough (equatorial calms, doldrums)
47 subtropical high-pressure belts (horse latitudes)
48 north-east trade winds (north-east trades, tropical easterlies)
49 south-east trade winds (south-east trades, tropical easterlies)
50 zones of the variable westerlies
51 polar wind zones
52 summer monsoon
53-58 **earth's climates**
53 equatorial climate: tropical zone (tropical rain zone)
54 the two arid zones (equatorial dry zones): desert and steppe zones
55 the two temperate rain zones
56 boreal climate (snow forest climate)
57-58 polar climates
57 tundra climate
58 perpetual frost climate

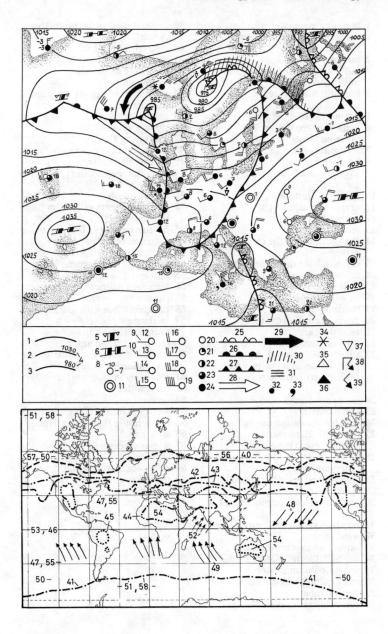

10 Meteorological Instruments

1 mercury barometer, a siphon barometer, a liquid–column barometer
2 mercury column
3 millibar scale (millimetre, *Am.* millimeter, scale)
4 barograph, a self–registering aneroid barometer
5 drum (recording drum)
6 bank of aneroid capsules (aneroid boxes)
7 recording arm
8 hygrograph
9 hygrometer element (hair element)
10 reading adjustment
11 amplitude adjustment
12 recording arm
13 recording pen
14 change gears for the clockwork drive
15 off switch for the recording arm
16 drum (recording drum)
17 time scale
18 case (housing)
19 thermograph
20 drum (recording drum)
21 recording arm
22 sensing element
23 silver–disc (silver–disk) pyrheliometer, an instrument for measuring the sun's radiant energy
24 silver disc (disk)
25 thermometer
26 wooden insulating casing
27 tube with diaphragm (diaphragmed tube)
28 wind gauge (*Am.* gage) (anemometer)
29 wind–speed indicator (wind–speed meter)
30 cross arms with hemispherical cups
31 wind–direction indicator
32 wind vane
33 aspiration psychrometer
34 dry bulb thermometer
35 wet bulb thermometer
36 solar radiation shielding
37 suction tube
38 recording rain gauge (*Am.* gage)

39 protective housing (protective casing)
40 collecting vessel
41 rain cover
42 recording mechanism
43 siphon tube
44 precipitation gauge (*Am.* gage) (rain gauge)
45 collecting vessel
46 storage vessel
47 measuring glass
48 insert for measuring snowfall
49 thermometer screen (thermometer shelter)
50 hygrograph
51 thermograph
52 psychrometer (wet and dry bulb thermometer)
53–54 thermometers for measuring extremes of temperature
53 maximum thermometer
54 minimum thermometer
55 radiosonde assembly
56 hydrogen balloon
57 parachute
58 radar reflector with spacing lines
59 instrument housing with radiosonde (a short–wave transmitter) and antenna
60 transmissometer, an instrument for measuring visibility
61 recording instrument (recorder)
62 transmitter
63 receiver
64 weather satellite (ITOS satellite)
65 temperature regulation flaps
66 solar panel
67 television camera
68 antenna
69 solar sensor (sun sensor)
70 telemetry antenna
71 radiometer

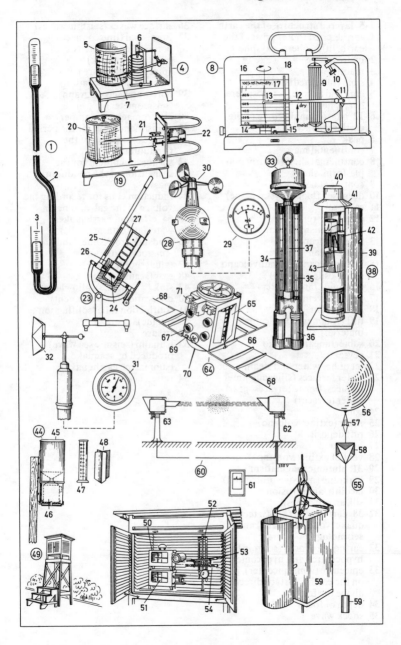

11 Physical Geography I

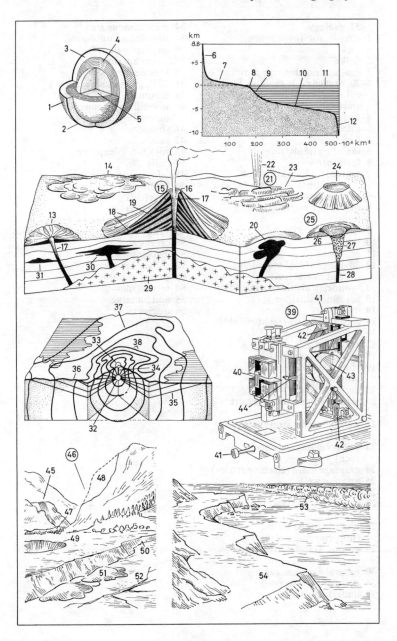

12 Physical Geography II

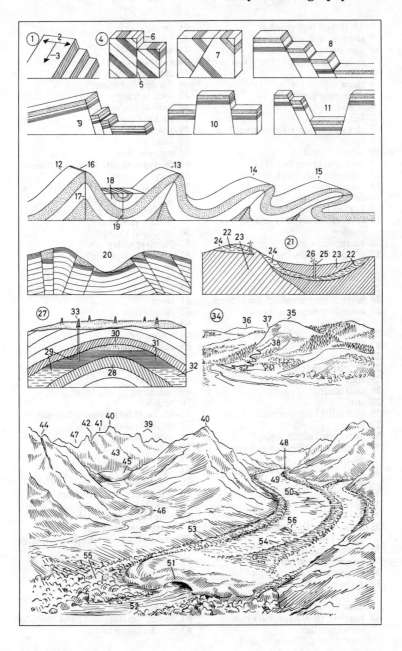

13 Physical Geography III

1–13 fluvial topography
1 river mouth, a delta
2 distributary (distributary channel), a river branch (river arm)
3 lake
4 bank
5 peninsula (spit)
6 island
7 bay (cove)
8 stream (brook, rivulet, creek)
9 levee
10 alluvial plain
11 meander (river bend)
12 meander core (rock island)
13 meadow
14–24 bog (marsh)
14 low–moor bog
15 layers of decayed vegetable matter
16 entrapped water
17 fen peat [consisting of rush and sedge]
18 alder–swamp peat
19 high–moor bog
20 layer of recent sphagnum mosses
21 boundary between layers (horizons)
22 layer of older sphagnum mosses
23 bog pool
24 swamp
25–31 cliffline (cliffs)
25 rock
26 sea (ocean)
27 surf
28 cliff (cliff face, steep rock face)
29 scree
30 [wave–cut] notch
31 abrasion platform (wave–cut platform)
32 atoll (ring–shaped coral reef), a coral reef
33 lagoon
34 breach (hole)
35–44 beach
35 high–water line (high–water mark, tidemark)
36 waves breaking on the shore
37 groyne (*Am.* groin)
38 groyne (*Am.* groin) head
39 wandering dune (migratory dune, travelling, *Am.* traveling, dune), a dune
40 barchan (barchane, barkhan, crescentic dune)

41 ripple marks
42 hummock
43 wind cripple
44 coastal lake
45 canyon (cañon, coulee)
46 plateau (tableland)
47 rock terrace
48 sedimentary rock (stratified rock)
49 river terrace (bed)
50 joint
51 canyon river
52–56 types of valley [cross section]
52 gorge (ravine)
53 V–shaped valley (V–valley)
54 widened V–shaped valley
55 U–shaped valley (U–valley, trough valley)
56 synclinal valley
57–70 river valley
57 scarp (escarpment)
58 slip–off slope
59 mesa
60 ridge
61 river
62 flood plain
63 river terrace
64 terracette
65 pediment
66 hill
67 valley floor (valley bottom)
68 riverbed
69 sediment
70 bedrock
71–83 karst formation in limestone
71 dolina, a sink (sinkhole, swallowhole)
72 polje
73 percolation of a river
74 karst spring
75 dry valley
76 system of caverns (system of caves)
77 water level (water table) in a karst formation
78 impervious rock (impermeable rock)
79 limestone cave (dripstone cave)
80–81 speleothems (cave formations)
80 stalactite (dripstone)
81 stalagmite
82 linked–up stalagmite and stalactite
83 subterranean river

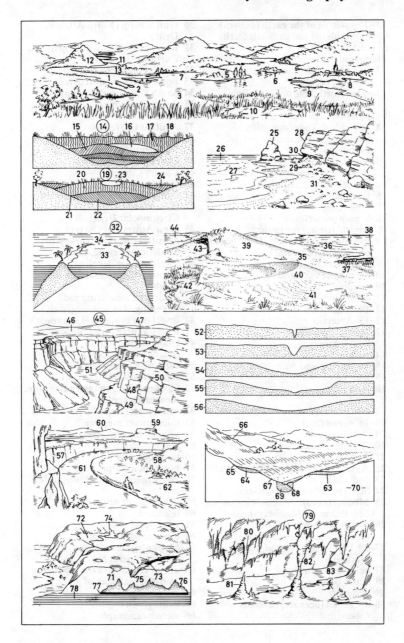

14 Map I

1-7 **graticule of the earth** (network of meridians and parallels on the earth's surface)
1 equator
2 line of latitude (parallel of latitude, parallel)
3 pole (North Pole or South Pole), a terrestrial pole (geographical pole)
4 line of longitude (meridian of longitude, meridian, terrestrial meridian)
5 Standard meridian (Prime meridian, Greenwich meridian, meridian of Greenwich)
6 latitude
7 longitude
8-9 **map projections**
8 conical (conic) projection
9 cylindrical projection (Mercator projection, Mercator's projection)
10-45 **map of the world**
10 tropics
11 polar circles
12-18 **continents**
12-13 America
12 North America
13 South America
14 Africa
15-16 Europe and Asia
15 Europe
16 Asia
17 Australia
18 Antarctica (Antarctic Continent)
19-26 **ocean** (sea)
19 Pacific Ocean
20 Atlantic Ocean
21 Arctic Ocean
22 Antarctic Ocean (Southern Ocean)
23 Indian Ocean
24 Strait of Gibraltar, a sea strait
25 Mediterranean (Mediterranean Sea, European Mediterranean)
26 North Sea, a marginal sea (epeiric sea, epicontinental sea)
27-29 **key (explanation of map symbols)**
27 cold ocean current
28 warm ocean current
29 scale
30-45 **ocean (oceanic) currents** (ocean drifts)
30 Gulf Stream (North Atlantic Drift)
31 Kuroshio (Kuro Siwo, Japan Current)
32 North Equatorial Current
33 Equatorial Countercurrent
34 South Equatorial Current
35 Brazil Current
36 Somali Current
37 Agulhas Current
38 East Australian Current
39 California Current
40 Labrador Current
41 Canary Current
42 Peru Current
43 Benguela (Benguella) Current
44 West Wind Drift (Antarctic Circumpolar Drift)
45 West Australian Current
46-62 **surveying** (land surveying, geodetic surveying, geodesy)
46 levelling (*Am.* leveling) (geometrical measurement of height)
47 graduated measuring rod (levelling, *Am.* leveling, staff)
48 level (surveying level, surveyor's level), a surveyor's telescope
49 triangulation station (triangulation point)
50 supporting scaffold
51 signal tower (signal mast)
52-62 **theodolite, an instrument for measuring angles**
52 micrometer head
53 micrometer eyepiece
54 vertical tangent screw
55 vertical clamp
56 tangent screw
57 horizontal clamp
58 adjustment for the illuminating mirror
59 illuminating mirror
60 telescope
61 spirit level
62 circular adjustment
63-66 **photogrammetry** (phototopography)
63 air survey camera for producing overlapping series of pictures
64 stereoscope
65 pantograph
66 stereoplanigraph

Map I 14

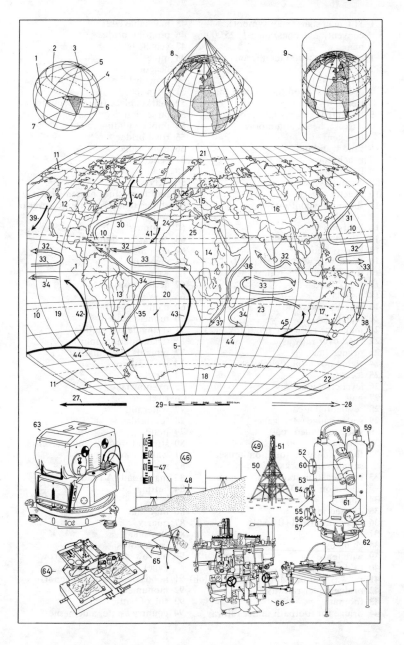

15 Map II

1–114 map signs (map symbols, conventional signs) on a 1 : 25 000 map

1 coniferous wood (coniferous trees)
2 clearing
3 forestry office
4 deciduous wood (non–coniferous trees)
5 heath (rough grassland, rough pasture, heath and moor, bracken)
6 sand (sand hills)
7 beach grass
8 lighthouse
9 mean low water
10 beacon
11 submarine contours
12 train ferry
13 lightship
14 mixed wood (mixed trees)
15 brushwood
16 motorway with slip road (*Am.* freeway with on–ramp)
17 trunk road
18 grassland
19 marshy grassland
20 marsh
21 main line railway (*Am.* trunk line)
22 road over railway
23 branch line
24 signal box (*Am.* switch tower)
25 local line
26 level crossing
27 halt
28 residential area
29 water gauge (*Am.* gage)
30 good, metalled road
31 windmill
32 thorn house (graduation house, salina, salt–works
33 broadcasting station (wireless or television mast)
34 mine
35 disused mine
36 secondary road (B road)
37 works
38 chimney
39 wire fence
40 bridge over railway
41 railway station (*Am.* railroad station)
42 bridge under railway
43 footpath
44 bridge for footpath under railway
45 navigable river
46 pontoon bridge
47 vehicle ferry
48 mole
49 beacon
50 stone bridge
51 town (city)
52 market place (market square)
53 large church
54 public building
55 road bridge
56 iron bridge
57 canal
58 lock
59 jetty
60 foot ferry (foot passenger ferry)
61 chapel (church) without tower or spire
62 contours
63 monastery (convent)
64 church landmark
65 vineyard
66 weir
67 aerial ropeway
68 view point
69 dam
70 tunnel
71 triangulation station (triangulation point)
72 remains of a building
73 wind pump
74 fortress
75 ox–bow lake
76 river
77 watermill
78 footbridge
79 pond
80 stream (brook, rivulet, creek)
81 water tower
82 spring
83 main road (A road)
84 cutting
85 cave
86 lime kiln
87 quarry
88 clay pit
89 brickworks
90 narrow–gauge (*Am.* narrow gage) railway
91 goods depot (freight depot)
92 monument
93 site of battle
94 country estate, a demesne

Map II 15

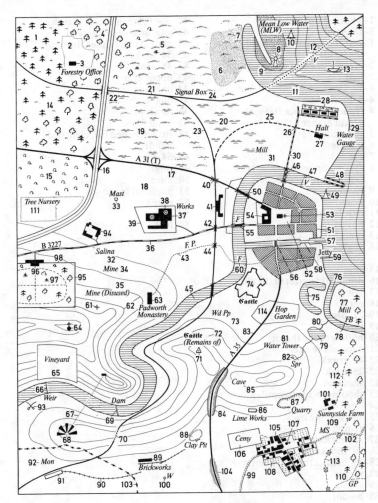

95 wall	**105** village
96 stately home	**106** cemetery
97 park	**107** church (chapel) with spire
98 hedge	**108** orchard
99 poor or unmetalled road	**109** milestone
100 well	**110** guide post
101 farm	**111** tree nursery
102 unfenced path (unfenced track)	**112** ride (aisle, lane, section line)
103 district boundary	**113** electricity transmission line
104 embankment	**114** hop garden

16 Man I

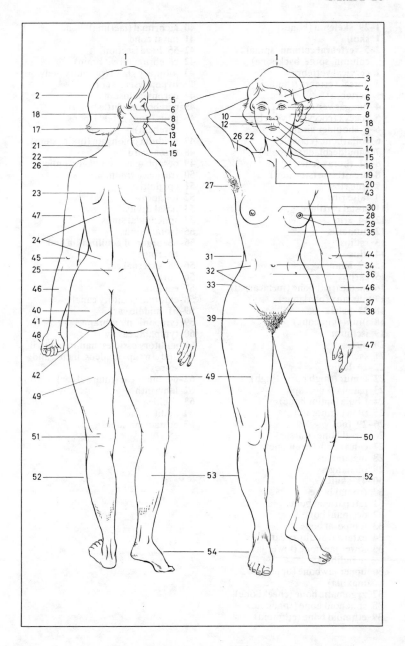

17 Man II

1–29 skeleton (bones)
1 skull
2–5 vertebral column (spinal column, spine, backbone)
2 cervical vertebra
3 dorsal vertebra (thoracic vertebra)
4 lumbar vertebra
5 coccyx (coccygeal vertebra)
6–7 shoulder girdle
6 collarbone (clavicle)
7 shoulderblade (scapula)
8–11 thorax (chest)
8 breastbone (sternum)
9 true ribs
10 false ribs
11 costal cartilage
12–14 arm
12 humerus
13 radius
14 ulna
15–17 hand
15 carpus
16 metacarpal bone (metacarpal)
17 phalanx (phalange)
18–21 pelvis
18 ilium (hip bone)
19 ischium
20 pubis
21 sacrum
22–25 leg
22 femur (thigh bone, thigh)
23 patella (kneecap)
24 fibula (splint bone)
25 tibia (shinbone)
26–29 foot
26 tarsal bones (tarsus)
27 calcaneum (heelbone)
28 metatarsus
29 phalanges
30–41 skull
30 frontal bone
31 left parietal bone
32 occipital bone
33 temporal bone
34 external auditory canal
35 lower jawbone (lower jaw, mandible)
36 upper jawbone (upper jaw, maxilla)
37 zygomatic bone (cheekbone)
38 sphenoid bone (sphenoid)
39 ethmoid bone (ethmoid)

40 lachrimal (lacrimal) bone
41 nasal bone
42–55 head [section]
42 cerebrum (great brain)
43 pituitary gland (pituitary body, hypophysis cerebri)
44 corpus callosum
45 cerebellum (little brain)
46 pons (pons cerebri, pons cerebelli)
47 medulla oblongata (brain–stem)
48 spinal cord
49 oesophagus (esophagus, gullet)
50 trachea (windpipe)
51 epiglottis
52 tongue
53 nasal cavity
54 sphenoidal sinus
55 frontal sinus
56–65 organ of equilibrium and hearing
56–58 external ear
56 auricle
57 ear lobe
58 external auditory canal
59–61 middle ear
59 tympanic membrane
60 tympanic cavity
61 auditory ossicles: hammer, anvil, and stirrup (malleus, incus, and stapes)
62–64 inner ear (internal ear)
62 labyrinth
63 cochlea
64 auditory nerve
65 eustachian tube

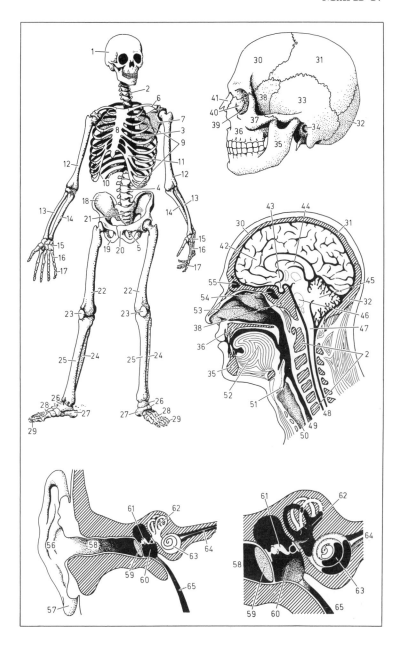

18 Man III

1-21 **blood circulation** (circulatory system)
1 common carotid artery, an artery
2 jugular vein, a vein
3 temporal artery
4 temporal vein
5 frontal artery
6 frontal vein
7 subclavian artery
8 subclavian vein
9 superior vena cava
10 arch of the aorta (aorta)
11 pulmonary artery [with venous blood]
12 pulmonary vein [with arterial blood]
13 lungs
14 heart
15 inferior vena cava
16 abdominal aorta (descending portion of the aorta)
17 iliac artery
18 iliac vein
19 femoral artery
20 tibial artery
21 radial artery
22-33 **nervous system**
22 cerebrum (great brain)
23 cerebellum (little brain)
24 medulla oblongata (brain-stem)
25 spinal cord
26 thoracic nerves
27 brachial plexus
28 radial nerve
29 ulnar nerve
30 great sciatic nerve [lying posteriorly]
31 femoral nerve (anterior crural nerve)
32 tibial nerve
33 peroneal nerve
34-64 **musculature** (muscular system)
34 sternocleidomastoid muscle (sternomastoid muscle)
35 deltoid muscle
36 pectoralis major (greater pectoralis muscle, greater pectoralis)
37 biceps brachii (biceps of the arm)
38 triceps brachii (triceps of the arm)
39 brachioradialis
40 flexor carpi radialis (radial flexor of the wrist)
41 thenar muscle
42 serratus anterior
43 obliquus externus abdominis (external oblique)
44 rectus abdominis
45 sartorius
46 vastus lateralis and vastus medialis
47 tibialis anterior
48 tendo calcanaeus (Achilles' tendon)
49 abductor hallucis (abductor of the hallux), a foot muscle
50 occipitalis
51 splenius of the neck
52 trapezius
53 infraspinatus
54 teres minor (lesser teres)
55 teres major (greater teres)
56 extensor carpi radialis longus (long radial extensor of the wrist)
57 extensor communis digitorum (common extensor of the digits)
58 flexor carpi ulnaris (ulnar flexor of the wrist)
59 latissimus dorsi
60 gluteus maximus
61 biceps femoris (biceps of the thigh)
62 gastrocnemius, medial and lateral heads
63 extensor communis digitorum (common extensor of the digits)
64 peroneus longus (long peroneus)

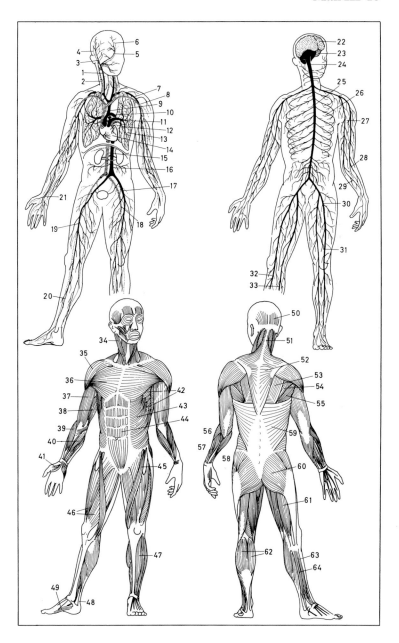

19 Man IV

1-13 head and neck
1 sternocleidomastoid muscle (sternomastoid muscle)
2 occipitalis
3 temporalis (temporal, temporal muscle)
4 occipito frontalis (frontalis)
5 orbicularis oculi
6 muscles of facial expression
7 masseter
8 orbicularis oris
9 parotid gland
10 lymph node (submandibular lymph gland)
11 submandibular gland (submaxillary gland)
12 muscles of the neck
13 Adam's apple (laryngeal prominence) [in men only]

14-37 mouth and throat
14 upper lip
15 gum
16-18 teeth (set of teeth)
16 incisors
17 canine tooth (canine)
18 premolar (bicuspid) and molar teeth (premolars and molars)
19 angle of the mouth (labial commissure)
20 hard palate
21 soft palate (velum palati, velum)
22 uvula
23 palatine tonsil (tonsil)
24 pharyngeal opening (pharynx, throat)
25 tongue
26 lower lip
27 upper jaw (maxilla)
28-37 tooth
28 periodontal membrane (periodontium, pericementum)
29 cement (dental cementum, crusta petrosa)
30 enamel
31 dentine (dentin)
32 dental pulp (tooth pulp, pulp)
33 nerves and blood vessels
34 incisor
35 molar tooth (molar)
36 root (fang)
37 crown
38-51 eye
38 eyebrow (supercilium)
39 upper eyelid (upper palpebra)
40 lower eyelid (lower palpebra)
41 eyelash (cilium)
42 iris
43 pupil

44 eye muscles (ocular muscles)
45 eyeball
46 vitreous body
47 cornea
48 lens
49 retina
50 blind spot
51 optic nerve
52-63 foot
52 big toe (great toe, first toe, hallux, digitus I)
53 second toe (digitus II)
54 third toe (digitus III)
55 fourth toe (digitus IV)
56 little toe (digitus minimus, digitus V)
57 toenail
58 ball of the foot
59 lateral malleolus (external malleolus, outer malleolus, malleolus fibulae)
60 medial malleolus (internal malleolus, inner malleolus, malleolus tibulae, malleolus medialis)
61 instep (medial longitudinal arch, dorsum of the foot, dorsum pedis)
62 sole of the foot
63 heel
64-83 hand
64 thumb (pollex, digitus I)
65 index finger (forefinger, second finger, digitus II)
66 middle finger (third finger, digitus medius, digitus III)
67 ring finger (fourth finger, digitus anularis, digitus IV)
68 little finger (fifth finger, digitus minimus, digitus V)
69 radial side of the hand
70 ulnar side of the hand
71 palm of the hand (palma manus)
72-74 lines of the hand
72 life line (line of life)
73 head line (line of the head)
74 heart line (line of the heart)
75 ball of the thumb (thenar eminence)
76 wrist (carpus)
77 phalanx (phalange)
78 finger pad
79 fingertip
80 fingernail (nail)
81 lunule (lunula) of the nail
82 knuckle
83 back of the hand (dorsum of the hand, dorsum manus)

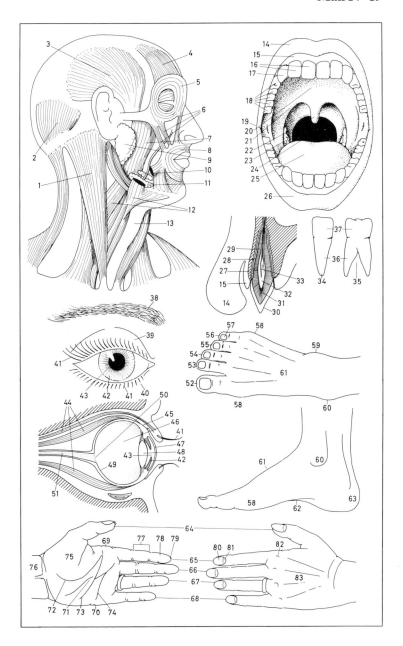

20 Man V

1-57 **internal organs** [front view]
1 thyroid gland
2–3 larynx
2 hyoid bone (hyoid)
3 thyroid cartilage
4 trachea (windpipe)
5 bronchus
6-7 lung
6 right lung
7 upper pulmonary lobe (upper lobe of the lung) [section]
8 heart
9 diaphragm
10 liver
11 gall bladder
12 spleen
13 stomach
14-22 **intestines** (bowel)
14-16 **small intestine** (intestinum tenue)
14 duodenum
15 jejunum
16 ileum
17-22 **large intestine** (intestinum crassum)
17 caecum (cecum)
18 appendix (vermiform appendix)
19 ascending colon
20 transverse colon
21 descending colon
22 rectum
23 oesophagus (esophagus, gullet)
24-25 heart
24 auricle
25 anterior longitudinal cardiac sulcus
26 diaphragm
27 spleen
28 right kidney
29 suprarenal gland
30-31 left kidney [longitudinal section]
30 calyx (renal calyx)
31 renal pelvis
32 ureter
33 bladder
34-35 liver [from behind]
34 falciform ligament of the liver
35 lobe of the liver
36 gall bladder
37-38 common bile duct
37 hepatic duct (common hepatic duct)
38 cystic duct
39 portal vein (hepatic portal vein)
40 oesophagus (esophagus, gullet)
41-42 stomach
41 cardiac orifice
42 pylorus
43 duodenum
44 pancreas

45-57 **heart** [longitudinal section]
45 atrium
46-47 valves of the heart
46 tricuspid valve (right atrioventricular valve)
47 bicuspid valve (mitral valve, left atrioventricular valve)
48 cusp
49 aortic valve
50 pulmonary valve
51 ventricle
52 ventricular septum (interventricular septum)
53 superior vena cava
54 aorta
55 pulmonary artery
56 pulmonary vein
57 inferior vena cava
58 peritoneum
59 sacrum
60 coccyx (coccygeal vertebra)
61 rectum
62 anus
63 anal sphincter
64 perineum
65 pubic symphisis (symphisis pubis)
66-77 **male sex organs** [longitudinal section]
66 penis
67 corpus cavernosum and spongiosum of the penis (erectile tissue of the penis)
68 urethra
69 glans penis
70 prepuce (foreskin)
71 scrotum
72 right testicle (testis)
73 epididymis
74 spermatic duct (vas deferens)
75 Cowper's gland (bulbourethral gland)
76 prostate (prostate gland)
77 seminal vesicle
78 bladder
79-88 **female sex organs** [longitudinal section]
79 uterus (matrix, womb)
80 cavity of the uterus
81 fallopian tube (uterine tube, oviduct)
82 fimbria (fimbriated extremity)
83 ovary
84 follicle with ovum (egg)
85 os uteri externum
86 vagina
87 lip of the pudendum (lip of the vulva)
88 clitoris

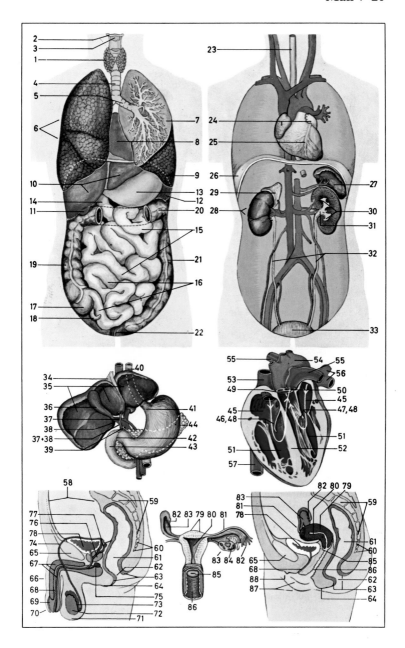

21 First Aid

1–13 emergency bandages
1 arm bandage
2 triangular cloth used as a sling (an arm sling)
3 head bandage (capeline)
4 first aid kit
5 first aid dressing
6 sterile gauze dressing
7 adhesive plaster (sticking plaster)
8 wound
9 bandage
10 emergency splint for a broken limb (fractured limb)
11 fractured leg (broken leg)
12 splint
13 headrest
14–17 measures for stanching the blood flow (tying up of, ligature of, a blood vessel)
14 pressure points of the arteries
15 emergency tourniquet on the thigh
16 walking stick used as a screw
17 compression bandage
18–23 rescue and transport of an injured person
18 Rautek grip (for rescue of victim of a car accident)
19 helper
20 injured person (casualty)
21 chair grip
22 carrying grip
23 emergency stretcher of sticks and a jacket
24–27 the positioning of an unconscious person and artificial respiration (resuscitation)
24 coma position
25 unconscious person
26 mouth–to–mouth resuscitation (*variation:* mouth–to–nose resuscitation)
27 resuscitator (respiratory apparatus, resuscitation apparatus), a respirator (artificial breathing device)
28–33 methods of rescue in ice accidents
28 person who has fallen through the ice
29 rescuer

30 rope
31 table (or similar device)
32 ladder
33 self–rescue
34–38 rescue of a drowning person
34 method of release (release grip, release) to free rescuer from the clutch of a drowning person
35 drowning person
36 lifesaver
37 chest grip, a towing grip
38 tired swimmer grip (hip grip)

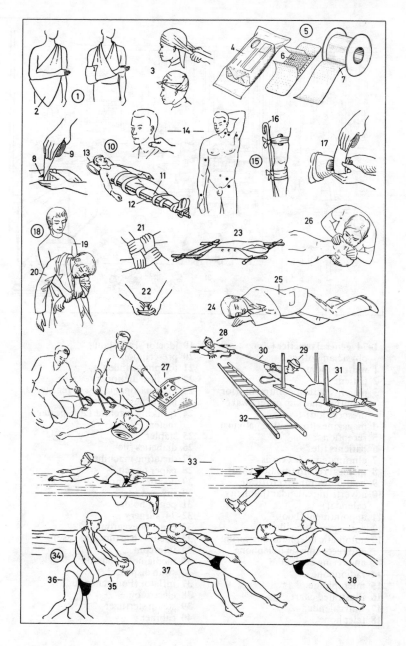

1–74 **general practice** (*Am.*
   physician's office)
1 **waiting room**
2 patient
3 patients with appointments (for
   a routine checkup or renewal of
   prescription)
4 magazines [for waiting patients]
5 reception
6 patients file
7 eliminated index cards
8 medical record (medical card)
9 health insurance certificate
10 advertising calendar (publicity
   calendar)
11 appointments book
12 correspondence file
13 automatic telephone answering
   and recording set (telephone
   answering device)
14 radiophone
15 microphone
16 illustrated chart
17 wall calendar
18 telephone

19 [doctor's] assistant
20 prescription
21 telephone index
22 medical dictionary
23 pharmacopoeia (list of registered
   medicines)
24 franking machine (*Am.* postage
   meter)
25 stapler
26 diabetics file
27 dictating machine
28 paper punch
29 doctor's stamp
30 ink pad
31 pencil holder
32–74 **surgery**
32 chart of eyegrounds
33 doctor's bag (doctor's case)
34 intercom
35 medicine cupboard
36 swab dispenser
37 inflator (Politzer bag)
38 electrotome
39 steam sterilizer
40 cabinet

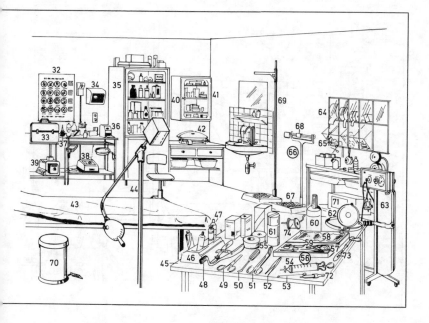

41 medicine samples	**61** thread container
42 baby scales	**62** ophthalmoscope
43 examination couch	**63** freezer for cryosurgery
44 directional lamp	**64** dispenser for plasters and small
45 instrument table	pieces of equipment
46 tube holder	**65** disposable hypodermic needles
47 tube of ointment	and syringes
48–50 instruments for minor	**66** scales, sliding–weight scales
surgery	**67** weighing platform
48 mouth gag	**68** sliding weight (jockey)
49 Kocher's forceps	**69** height gauge (*Am.* gage)
50 scoop (curette)	**70** waste bin (*Am.* trash bin)
51 angled scissors	**71** hot–air sterilizer
52 forceps	**72** pipette
53 olive–pointed (bulb–headed)	**73** percussor
probe	**74** aural speculum (auriscope, aural
54 syringe for irrigations of the ear	syringe)
or bladder	
55 adhesive plaster (sticking	
plaster)	
56 surgical suture material	
57 curved surgical needle	
58 sterile gauze	
59 needle holder	
60 spray for disinfecting the skin	

23 Doctor II

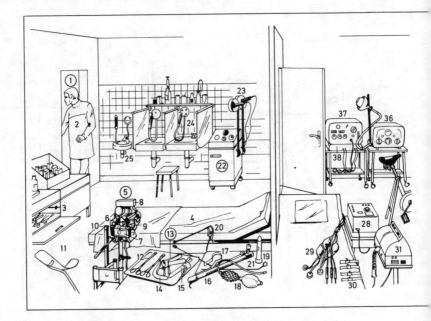

1 consulting room
2 general practitioner
3–21 instruments for gynecological and proctological examinations
3 warming the instruments up to body temperature
4 examination couch
5 colposcope
6 binocular eyepiece
7 miniature camera
8 cold light source
9 cable release
10 bracket for the leg support
11 leg support (leg holder)
12 holding forceps (sponge holder)
13 vaginal speculum
14 lower blade of the vaginal speculum
15 platinum loop (for smears)
16 rectoscope
17 biopsy forceps used with the rectoscope (proctoscope)

18 insufflator for proctoscopy (rectoscopy)
19 proctoscope (rectal speculum)
20 urethroscope
21 guide for inserting the proctoscope
22 diathermy unit (short–wave therapy apparatus)
23 radiator
24 inhaling apparatus (inhalator)
25 basin (for sputum)
26–31 ergometry
26 bicycle ergometer
27 monitor (visual display of the ECG and of pulse and respiratory rates when performing work)
28 ECG (electrocardiograph)
29 suction electrodes
30 strap-on electrodes for the limbs
31 spirometer (for measuring respiratory functions)
32 measuring the blood pressure

33 sphygmomanometer
34 inflatable cuff
35 stethoscope
36 microwave treatment unit
37 faradization unit (application of low-frequency currents with different pulse shapes)
38 automatic tuner
39 short-wave therapy apparatus
40 timer
41–59 laboratory
41 medical laboratory technician
42 capillary tube stand for blood sedimentation
43 measuring cylinder
44 automatic pipette
45 kidney dish
46 portable ECG machine for emergency use
47 automatic pipetting device
48 constant temperature water bath
49 tap with water jet pump

50 staining dish (for staining blood smears, sediments and other smears)
51 binocular research microscope
52 pipette stand for photometry
53 computer and analyser for photometry
54 photometer
55 potentiometric recorder
56 transforming section
57 laboratory apparatus (laboratory equipment)
58 urine sediment chart
59 centrifuge

24 Dentist

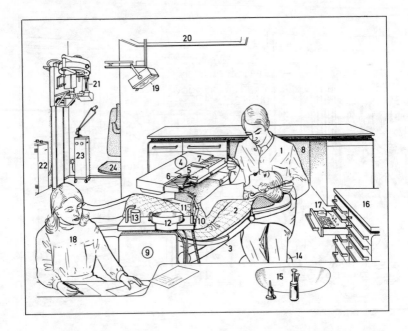

1 dentist (dental surgeon)
2 patient
3 dentist's chair
4 dental instruments
5 instrument tray
6 drills with different handpieces
7 medicine case
8 storage unit (for dental instruments)
9 assistant's unit
10 multi–purpose syringe (for cold and warm water, spray or air)
11 suction apparatus
12 basin
13 water glass, filled automatically
14 stool
15 washbasin
16 instrument cabinet
17 drawer for drills
18 dentist's assistant
19 dentist's lamp
20 ceiling light
21 X–ray apparatus for panoramic pictures

22 X–ray generator
23 microwave treatment unit, a radiation unit
24 seat
25 denture (set of false teeth)
26 bridge (dental bridge)
27 prepared stump of the tooth
28 crown (*kinds:* gold crown, jacket crown)
29 porcelain tooth (porcelain pontic)
30 filling
31 post crown
32 facing
33 diaphragm
34 post
35 carborundum disc (disk)
36 grinding wheel
37 burs
38 flame–shaped finishing bur
39 fissure burs
40 diamond point
41 mouth mirror
42 mouth lamp

43 cautery
44 platinum–iridium electrode
45 tooth scalers
46 probe
47 extraction forceps
48 tooth–root elevator
49 bone chisel
50 spatula
51 mixer for filling material
52 synchronous timer
53 hypodermic syringe for injection
   of local anaesthetic
54 hypodermic needle
55 matrix holder
56 impression tray
57 spirit lamp

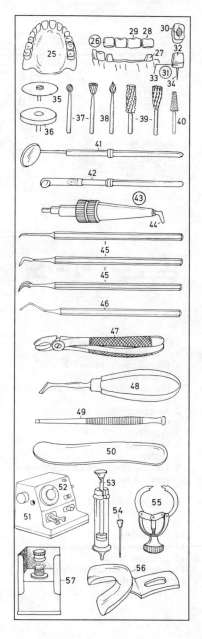

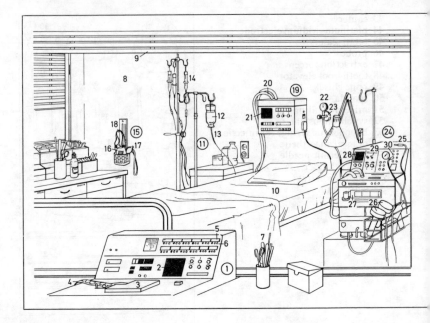

1–30 intensive care unit
1–9 control room
1 central control unit for monitoring heart rhythm (cardiac rhythm) and blood pressure
2 electrocardiogram monitor (ECG monitor)
3 recorder
4 recording paper
5 patient's card
6 indicator lights (with call buttons for each patient)
7 spatula
8 window (observation window, glass partition)
9 blind
10 bed (hospital bed)
11 stand for infusion apparatus
12 infusion bottle
13 tube for intravenous drips
14 infusion device for water-soluble medicaments
15 sphygmomanometer
16 cuff
17 inflating bulb
18 mercury manometer
19 bed monitor
20 connecting lead to the central control unit
21 electrocardiogram monitor (ECG monitor)
22 manometer for the oxygen supply
23 wall connection for oxygen treatment
24 mobile monitoring unit
25 electrode lead to the short-term pacemaker
26 electrodes for shock treatment
27 ECG recording unit
28 electrocardiogram monitor (ECG monitor)
29 control switches and knobs (controls) for adjusting the monitor

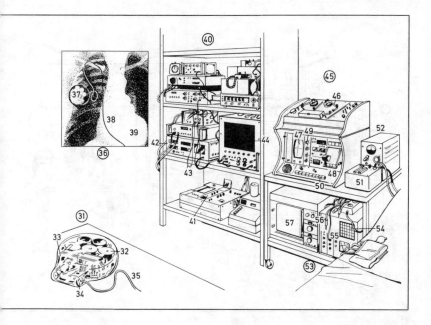

30 control buttons for the pacemaker unit
31 **pacemaker** (cardiac pacemaker)
32 mercury battery
33 programmed impulse generator
34 electrode exit point
35 electrode
36 implantation of the pacemaker
37 internal cardiac pacemaker (internal pacemaker, pacemaker)
38 electrode inserted through the vein
39 cardiac silhouette on the X-ray
40 **pacemaker control unit**
41 electrocardiograph (ECG recorder)
42 automatic impulse meter
43 ECG lead to the patient
44 monitor unit for visual monitoring of the pacemaker impulses
45 long-term ECG analyser

46 magnetic tape for recording the ECG impulses during analysis
47 ECG monitor
48 automatic analysis on paper of the ECG rhythm
49 control knob for the ECG amplitude
50 program selector switches for the ECG analysis
51 charger for the pacemaker batteries
52 battery tester
53 pressure gauge (*Am.* gage) for the right cardiac catheter
54 trace monitor
55 pressure indicator
56 connecting lead to the paper recorder
57 paper recorder for pressure traces

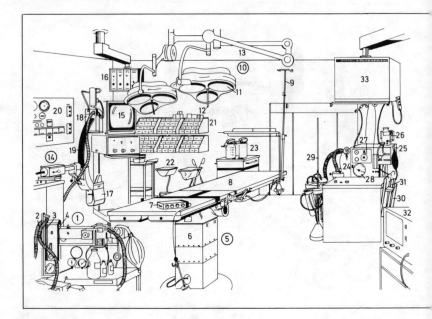

1-54 surgical unit
1-33 operating theatre (*Am.* theater)
1 anaesthesia and breathing apparatus (respiratory machine)
2 inhalers (inhaling tubes)
3 flowmeter for nitrous oxide
4 oxygen flow meter
5 pedestal operating table
6 table pedestal
7 control device (control unit)
8 adjustable top of the operating table
9 stand for intravenous drips
10 swivel-mounted shadow-free operating lamp
11 individual lamp
12 handle
13 swivel arm
14 mobile fluoroscope
15 monitor of the image converter
16 monitor [back]
17 tube
18 image converter
19 C-shaped frame
20 control panel for the air-conditioning
21 surgical suture material
22 mobile waste tray
23 containers for unsterile (unsterilized) pads
24 anaesthesia and respiratory apparatus
25 respirator
26 fluothane container (halothane container)
27 ventilation control knob
28 indicator with pointer for respiratory volume
29 stand with inhalers (inhaling tubes) and pressure gauges (*Am.* gages)
30 catheter holder
31 catheter in sterile packing

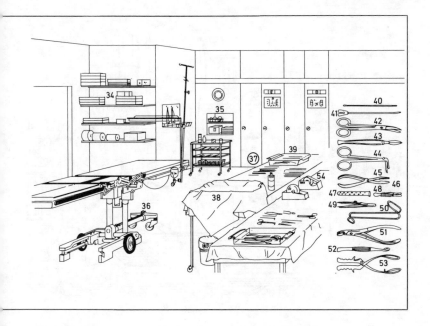

32 sphygmograph
33 monitor
34–54 preparation and sterilization room
34 dressing material
35 small sterilizer
36 carriage of the operating table
37 mobile instrument table
38 sterile cloth
39 instrument tray
40–53 surgical instruments
40 olive–pointed (bulb–headed) probe
41 hollow probe
42 curved scissors
43 scalpel (surgical knife)
44 ligature–holding forceps
45 sequestrum forceps
46 jaw
47 drainage tube
48 surgeon's tourniquet
49 artery forceps

50 blunt hook
51 bone nippers (bone–cutting forceps)
52 scoop (curette) for erasion (curettage)
53 obstetrical forceps
54 roll of plaster

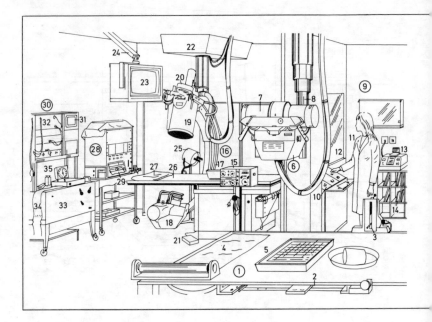

1–35 X-ray unit
1 X-ray examination table
2 support for X-ray cassettes
3 height adjustment of the central beam for lateral views
4 compress for pyelography and cholecystography
5 instrument basin
6 X-ray apparatus for pyelograms
7 X-ray tube
8 telescopic X-ray support
9 central X-ray control unit
10 control panel (control desk)
11 radiographer (X-ray technician)
12 window to the angiography room
13 oxymeter
14 pyelogram cassettes
15 contrast medium injector
16 X-ray image intensifier
17 C-shaped frame
18 X-ray head with X-ray tube
19 image converter with converter tube

20 film camera
21 foot switch
22 mobile mounting
23 monitor
24 swivel-mounted monitor support
25 operating lamp
26 angiographic examination table
27 pillow
28 eight-channel recorder
29 recording paper
30 catheter gauge (*Am.* gage) unit for catheterization of the heart
31 six-channel monitor for pressure graphs and ECG
32 slide-in units of the pressure transducer
33 paper recorder unit with developer for photographic recording
34 recording paper
35 timer

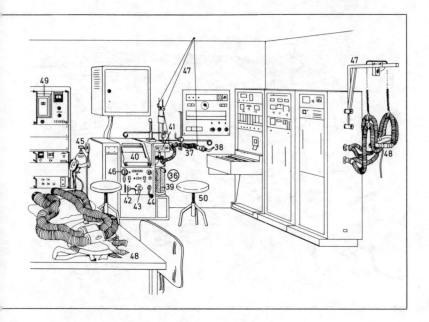

36–50 spirometry
36 spirograph for pulmonary
 function tests
37 breathing tube
38 mouthpiece
39 soda–lime absorber
40 recording paper
41 control knobs for gas supply
42 O₂–stabilizer
43 throttle valve
44 absorber attachment
45 oxygen cylinder
46 water supply
47 tube support
48 mask
49 CO₂ consumption meter
50 stool for the patient

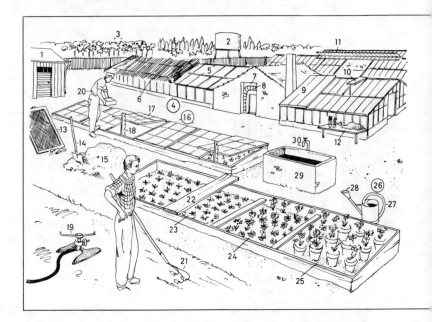

1–51 market garden (*Am.* truck garden, truck farm)
1 tool shed
2 water tower (water tank)
3 market garden (*Am.* truck garden, truck farm), a tree nursery
4 hothouse (forcing house, warm house)
5 glass roof
6 matting, e.g. straw matting, reed matting
7 boiler room (boiler house)
8 heating pipe (pressure pipe)
9 shading panel (shutter)
10–11 ventilators (vents)
10 ventilation window (window vent, hinged ventilator)
11 ridge vent
12 potting table (potting bench)
13 riddle (sieve, garden sieve, upright sieve)
14 garden shovel (shovel)
15 heap of earth (composted earth, prepared earth, garden mould, *Am.* mold)
16 hotbed (forcing bed, heated frame)
17 hotbed vent (frame vent)
18 vent prop
19 sprinkler (sprinkling device)
20 gardener (nursery gardener, grower, commercial grower)
21 cultivator (hand cultivator, grubber)
22 plank
23 pricked-out seedlings (pricked-off seedlings)
24 forced flowers [forcing]
25 potted plants (plants in pots, pot plants)
26 watering can (*Am.* sprinkling can)
27 handle
28 rose
29 water tank

30 water pipe
31 bale of peat
32 warm house (heated greenhouse)
33 cold house (unheated greenhouse)
34 wind generator
35 wind wheel
36 wind vane
37 shrub bed, a flower bed
38 hoop edging
39 vegetable plot
40 plastic tunnel (polythene greenhouse)
41 ventilation flap
42 central path
43 vegetable crate
44 tomato plant
45 nursery hand
46 nursery hand
47 tub plant
48 tub

49 orange tree
50 wire basket
51 seedling box

29 Garden Tools

1 dibber (dibble)
2 spade
3 lawn rake (wire-tooth rake)
4 rake
5 ridging hoe
6 trowel
7 combined hoe and fork
8 sickle
9 gardener's knife (pruning knife, billhook)
10 asparagus cutter (asparagus knife)
11 tree pruner (long-handled pruner)
12 semi-automatic spade
13 three-pronged cultivator
14 tree scraper (bark scraper)
15 lawn aerator (aerator)
16 pruning saw (saw for cutting branches)
17 battery-operated hedge trimmer
18 motor cultivator
19 electric drill
20 gear
21 cultivator attachment
22 fruit picker
23 tree brush (bark brush)
24 sprayer for pest control
25 lance
26 hose reel (reel and carrying cart)
27 garden hose
28 motor lawn mower (motor mower)
29 grassbox
30 two-stroke motor
31 electric lawn mower (electric mower)
32 electric lead (electric cable)
33 cutting unit
34 hand mower
35 cutting cylinder
36 blade
37 riding mower
38 brake lock
39 electric starter
40 brake pedal
41 cutting unit
42 tip-up trailer
43 revolving sprinkler, a lawn sprinkler
44 revolving nozzle
45 hose connector
46 oscillating sprinkler
47 wheelbarrow
48 grass shears
49 hedge shears
50 secateurs (pruning shears)

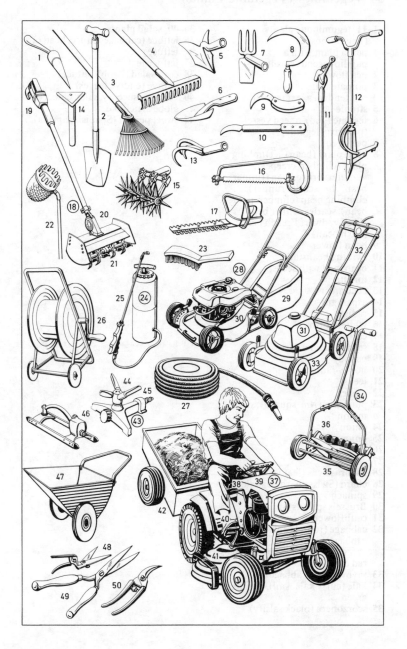

30 Vegetables (Vegetable Plants)

1-11 leguminous plants
(Leguminosae)
1 pea, a plant with a
   papilionaceous corolla
2 pea flower
3 pinnate leaf
4 pea tendril, a leaf tendril
5 stipule
6 legume (pod), a seed vessel
   (pericarp, legume)
7 pea [seed]
8 bean plant (bean), a climbing
   plant (climber, creeper);
   varieties: broad bean (runner
   bean, *Am.* scarlet runner),
   climbing bean (climber, pole
   bean), scarlet runner bean;
   smaller: dwarf French bean
   (bush bean)
9 bean flower
10 twining beanstalk
11 bean [pod with seeds]
12 tomato
13 cucumber
14 asparagus
15 radish
16 white radish
17 carrot
18 stump-rooted carrot
19 parsley
20 horse-radish
21 leeks
22 chives
23 pumpkin (*Am.* squash); *sim.:*
   melon
24 onion
25 onion skin
26 kohlrabi
27 celeriac
28-34 brassicas (leaf vegetables)
28 chard (Swiss chard, seakale beet)
29 spinach
30 Brussels sprouts (sprouts)
31 cauliflower
32 cabbage (round cabbage, head of
   cabbage), a brassica; *cultivated
   races (cultivars):* green cabbage,
   red cabbage
33 savoy (savoy cabbage)
34 kale (curly kale, kail), a winter
   green
35 scorzonera (black salsify)

36-40 salad plants
36 lettuce (cabbage lettuce, head of
   lettuce)
37 lettuce leaf
38 corn salad (lamb's lettuce)
39 endive (endive leaves)
40 chicory (succory, salad chicory)
41 globe artichoke
42 sweet pepper (Spanish paprika)

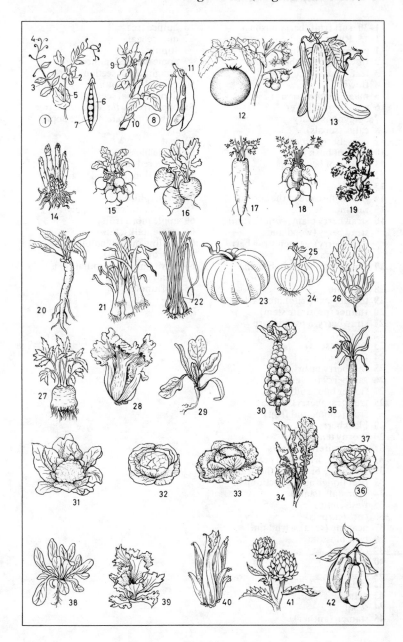

31 Soft Fruit and Pomes

1–30 **soft fruit** (berry bushes)
1–15 **Ribes**
1 gooseberry bush
2 flowering gooseberry cane
3 leaf
4 flower
5 magpie moth larva
6 gooseberry flower
7 epigynous ovary
8 calyx (sepals)
9 gooseberry, a berry
10 currant bush
11 cluster of berries
12 currant
13 stalk
14 flowering cane of the currant
15 raceme
16 strawberry plant; *varieties:* wild strawberry (woodland strawberry), garden strawberry, alpine strawberry
17 flowering and fruit-bearing plant
18 rhizome
19 ternate leaf (trifoliate leaf)
20 runner (prostrate stem)
21 strawberry, a pseudocarp
22 epicalyx
23 achene (seed)
24 flesh (pulp)
25 raspberry bush
26 raspberry flower
27 flower bud (bud)
28 fruit (raspberry), an aggregate fruit (compound fruit)
29 blackberry
30 thorny tendril
31–61 **pomiferous plants**
31 pear tree; *wild:* wild pear tree
32 flowering branch of the pear tree
33 pear [longitudinal section]
34 pear stalk (stalk)
35 flesh (pulp)
36 core (carpels)
37 pear pip (seed), a fruit pip
38 pear blossom
39 ovules
40 ovary
41 stigma
42 style
43 petal
44 sepal
45 stamen (anther)

46 quince tree
47 quince leaf
48 stipule
49 apple-shaped quince [longitudinal section]
50 pear-shaped quince [longitudinal section]
51 apple tree; *wild:* crab apple tree
52 flowering branch of the apple tree
53 leaf
54 apple blossom
55 withered flower
56 apple [longitudinal section]
57 apple skin
58 flesh (pulp)
59 core (apple core, carpels)
60 apple pip, a fruit pip
61 apple stalk (stalk)
62 codling moth (codlin moth)
63 burrow (tunnel)
64 larva (grub, caterpillar) of a small moth
65 wormhole

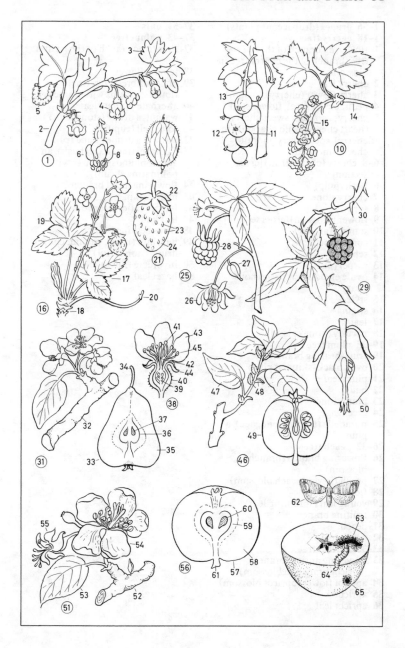

32 Drupes and Nuts

1–36 **drupes** (drupaceous plants)
1–18 **cherry tree**
1 flowering branch of the cherry tree (branch of the cherry tree in blossom)
2 cherry leaf
3 cherry flower (cherry blossom)
4 peduncle (pedicel, flower stalk)
5 cherry; *varieties:* sweet cherry (heart cherry), wild cherry (bird cherry), sour cherry, morello cherry (morello)
6–8 **cherry** (cherry fruit) [cross section]
6 flesh (pulp)
7 cherry stone
8 seed
9 flower (blossom) [cross section]
10 stamen (anther)
11 corolla (petals)
12 sepal
13 carpel (pistil)
14 ovule enclosed in perigynous ovary
15 style
16 stigma
17 leaf
18 nectary (honey gland)
19–23 **plum tree**
19 fruit-bearing branch
20 oval, black-skinned plum
21 plum leaf
22 bud
23 plum stone
24 greengage
25 mirabelle (transparent gage), a plum
26–32 **peach tree**
26 flowering branch (branch in blossom)
27 peach flower (peach blossom)
28 flower shoot
29 young leaf (sprouting leaf)
30 fruiting branch
31 peach
32 peach leaf
33–36 **apricot tree**
33 flowering apricot branch (apricot branch in blossom)
34 apricot flower (apricot blossom)
35 apricot
36 apricot leaf

37–51 **nuts**
37–43 **walnut tree**
37 flowering branch of the walnut tree
38 female flower
39 male inflorescence (male flowers, catkins with stamens)
40 alternate pinnate leaf
41 walnut, a drupe (stone fruit)
42 soft shell (cupule)
43 walnut, a drupe (stone fruit)
44–51 **hazel tree** (hazel bush), an anemophilous shrub (a wind-pollinating shrub)
44 flowering hazel branch
45 male catkin
46 female inflorescence
47 leaf bud
48 fruit-bearing branch
49 hazelnut (hazel, cobnut, cob), a drupe (stone fruit)
50 involucre (husk)
51 hazel leaf

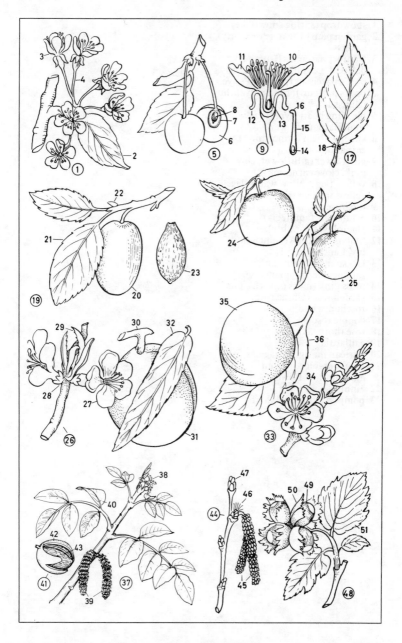

33 Garden Flowers

1 snowdrop (spring snowflake)
2 garden pansy (heartsease pansy), a pansy
3 trumpet narcissus (trumpet daffodil, Lent lily), a narcissus
4 poet's narcissus (pheasant's eye, poet's daffodil); *sim.:* polyanthus narcissus
5 bleeding heart (lyre flower), a fumariaceous flower
6 sweet william (bunch pink), a carnation
7 gillyflower (gilliflower, clove pink, clove carnation)
8 yellow flag (yellow water flag, yellow iris), an iris
9 tuberose
10 columbine (aquilegia)
11 gladiolus (sword lily)
12 Madonna lily (Annunciation lily, Lent lily), a lily
13 larkspur (delphinium), a ranunculaceous plant
14 moss pink (moss phlox), a phlox
15 garden rose (China rose)
16 rosebud, a bud
17 double rose
18 rose thorn, a thorn
19 gaillardia
20 African marigold (tagetes)
21 love-lies-bleeding, an amaranthine flower
22 zinnia
23 pompon dahlia, a dahlia

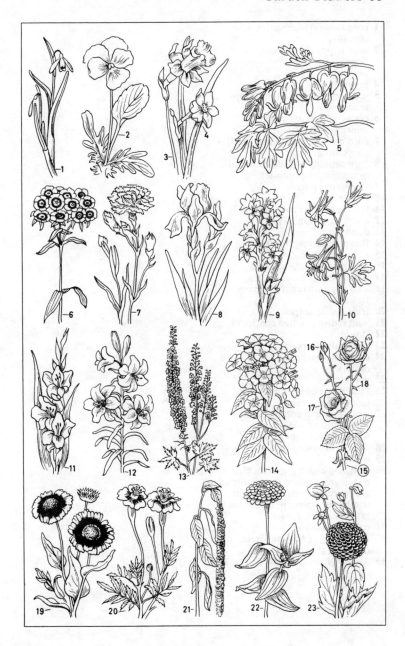

34 Weeds

1 corn flower (bluebottle), a centaury
2 corn poppy (field poppy), a poppy
3 bud
4 poppy flower
5 seed capsule containing poppy seeds
6 corn cockle (corn campion, crown-of-the-field)
7 corn marigold (field marigold), a chrysanthemum
8 corn camomile (field camomile, camomile, chamomile)
9 shepherd's purse
10 flower
11 fruit (pouch-shaped pod)
12 common groundsel
13 dandelion
14 flower head (capitulum)
15 infructescence
16 hedge mustard, a mustard
17 stonecrop
18 wild mustard (charlock, runch)
19 flower
20 fruit, a siliqua (pod)
21 wild radish (jointed charlock)
22 flower
23 fruit (siliqua, pod)
24 common orache (common orach)
25 goosefoot
26 field bindweed (wild morning glory), a bindweed
27 scarlet pimpernel (shepherd's weatherglass, poor man's weatherglass, eye-bright)
28 wild barley (wall barley)
29 wild oat
30 common couch grass (couch, quack grass, quick grass, quitch grass, scutch grass, twitch grass, witchgrass); *sim.:* bearded couch grass, sea couch grass
31 gallant soldier
32 field eryngo (Watling Street thistle), a thistle
33 stinging nettle, a nettle

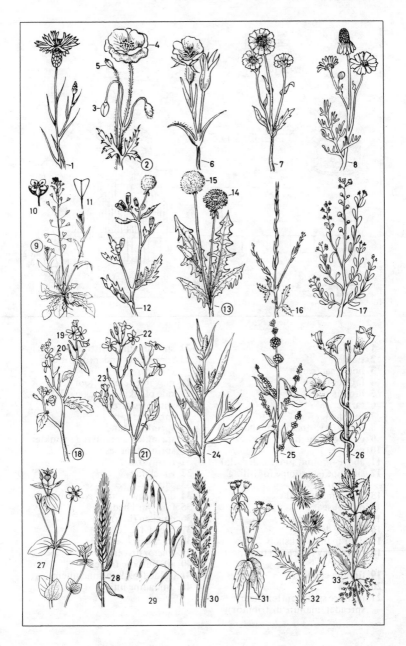

35 Farm Buildings (*Am.* Farmstead)

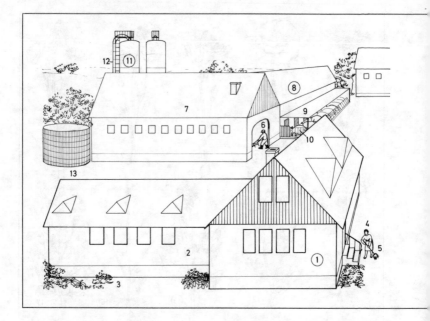

1 house
2 stable
3 house cat (cat)
4 farmer's wife
5 broom
6 farmer
7 cowshed
8 pigsty (sty, *Am.* pigpen, hogpen)
9 outdoor trough
10 pig
11 above–ground silo (fodder silo)
12 silo pipe (standpipe for filling the silo)
13 liquid manure silo
14 outhouse
15 machinery shed
16 sliding door
17 door to the workshop
18 three–way tip-cart, a transport vehicle
19 tipping cylinder
20 shafts
21 manure spreader (fertilizer spreader, manure distributor)

22 spreader unit (distributor unit)
23 spreader cylinder (distributor cylinder)
24 movable scraper floor
25 side planking (side board)
26 wire mesh front
27 sprinkler cart
28 sprinkler stand
29 sprinkler, a revolving sprinkler
30 sprinkler hoses
31 farmyard
32 watchdog
33 calf
34 dairy cow (milch-cow, milker)
35 farmyard hedge
36 chicken (hen)
37 cock (*Am.* rooster)
38 tractor
39 tractor driver
40 all–purpose trailer
41 [folded] pickup attachment
42 unloading unit

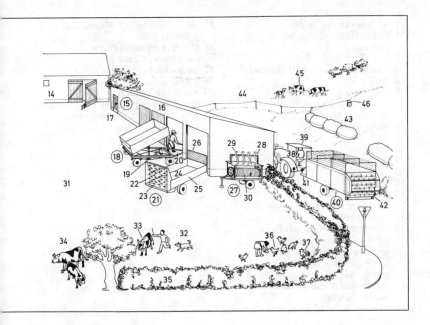

43 polythene silo, a fodder silo
44 meadow
45 grazing cattle
46 electrified fence

36 Agriculture (Farming)

1-41 work in the fields
1 fallow (fallow field, fallow ground)
2 boundary stone
3 boundary ridge, a balk (baulk)
4 field
5 farmworker (agricultural worker, farmhand, farm labourer, *Am.* laborer)
6 plough (*Am.* plow)
7 clod
8 furrow
9 stone
10-12 sowing
10 sower
11 seedlip
12 seed corn (seed)
13 field guard
14 chemical fertilizer (artificial fertilizer); *kinds:* potash fertilizer, phosphoric acid fertilizer, lime fertilizer, nitrogen fertilizer
15 cartload of manure (farmyard manure, dung)
16 oxteam (team of oxen, *Am.* span of oxen)
17 fields (farmland)
18 farm track (farm road)
19-30 hay harvest (haymaking)
19 rotary mower with swather (swath reaper)
20 connecting shaft (connecting rod)
21 power take-off (power take-off shaft)
22 meadow
23 swath (swathe)
24 tedder (rotary tedder)
25 tedded hay
26 rotary swather
27 trailer with pickup attachment
28 fence rack (rickstand), a drying rack for hay
29 rickstand, a drying rack for hay
30 hay tripod
31-41 grain harvest and seedbed preparation
31 combine harvester
32 cornfield
33 stubble field
34 bale of straw

35 straw baler (straw press), a high-pressure baler
36 swath (swathe) of straw (windrow of straw)
37 hydraulic bale loader
38 trailer
39 manure spreader
40 four-furrow plough (*Am.* plow)
41 combination seed-harrow

37 Agricultural Machinery I

1-33 **combine harvester** (combine)
1 divider
2 grain lifter
3 cutter bar
4 pickup reel, a spring-tine reel
5 reel gearing
6 auger
7 chain and slat elevator
8 hydraulic cylinder for adjusting the cutting unit
9 stone catcher (stone trap)
10 awner
11 concave
12 threshing drum (drum)
13 revolving beater [for freeing straw from the drum and preparing it for the shakers]
14 straw shaker (strawwalker)
15 fan for compressed-air winnowing
16 preparation level
17 louvred-type sieve
18 sieve extension
19 shoe sieve (reciprocating sieve)
20 grain auger
21 tailings auger
22 tailings outlet
23 grain tank
24 grain tank auger
25 augers feeding to the grain tank unloader
26 grain unloader spout
27 observation ports for checking tank contents
28 six-cylinder diesel engine
29 hydraulic pump with oil reservoir
30 driving axle gearing
31 driving wheel tyre (*Am.* tire)
32 rubber-tyred (*Am.* rubber-tired) wheel on the steering axle
33 driver's position
34-39 **self-propelled forage harvester** (self-propelled field chopper)
34 cutting drum (chopper drum)
35 corn head
36 cab (driver's cab)
37 swivel-mounted spout (discharge pipe)
38 exhaust
39 rear-wheel steering system
40-45 **rotary swather**
40 cardan shaft
41 running wheel
42 double spring tine
43 crank
44 swath rake
45 three-point linkage
46-58 **rotary tedder**
46 tractor
47 draw bar
48 cardan shaft

49 power take-off (power take-off shaft)
50 gearing (gears)
51 frame bar
52 rotating head
53 tine bar
54 double spring tine
55 guard rail
56 running wheel
57 height adjustment crank
58 wheel adjustment
59-84 **potato harvester**
59 control levers for the lifters of the digger and the hopper and for adjusting the shaft
60 adjustable hitch
61 drawbar
62 drawbar support
63 cardan shaft connection
64 press roller
65 gearing (gears) for the hydraulic system
66 disc (disk) coulter (*Am.* colter) (rolling coulter)
67 three-bladed share
68 disc (disk) coulter (*Am.* colter) drive
69 open-web elevator
70 agitator
71 multi-step reduction gearing
72 feeder
73 haulm stripper (flail rotor)
74 rotary elevating drum
75 mechanical tumbling separator
76 haulm conveyor with flexible haulm strippers
77 haulm conveyor agitator
78 haulm conveyor drive with V-belt
79 studded rubber belt for sorting vines, clods and stones
80 trash conveyor
81 sorting table
82 rubber-disc (rubber-disk) rollers for presorting
83 discharge conveyor
84 endless-floor hopper
85-96 **beet harvester**
85 topper
86 feeler
87 topping knife
88 feeler support wheel with depth adjustment
89 beet cleaner
90 haulm elevator
91 hydraulic pump
92 compressed-air reservoir
93 oil tank (oil reservoir)
94 tensioning device for the beet elevator
95 beet elevator belt
96 beet hopper

38 Agricultural Machinery II

1 **wheel plough** (*Am.* plow),
  a single-bottom plough *[form.]*
2 handle
3 plough (*Am.* plow) stilt (plough
  handle)
4-8 plough (*Am.* **plow) bottom**
4 mouldboard (*Am.* moldboard)
5 landside
6 sole (slade)
7 ploughshare (share, *Am.*
  plowshare)
8 frog (frame)
9 beam (plough beam, *Am.*
  plowbeam)
10 knife coulter (*Am.* colter),
  a coulter
11 skim coulter (*Am.* colter)
12 guide-chain crossbar
13 guide chain
14-19 forecarriage
14 adjustable yoke (yoke)
15 land wheel
16 furrow wheel
17 hake chain
18 draught beam (drawbar)
19 hake
20 **tractor** (general-purpose tractor)
21 cab frame (roll bar)
22 seat
23 power take-off gear-change
  (gearshift)
24-29 power lift
24 ram piston
25 lifting rod adjustment
26 drawbar frame
27 top link
28 lower link
29 lifting rod
30 drawbar coupling
31 live power take-off (live power
  take-off shaft, take-off shaft)
32 differential gear (differential)
33 floating axle
34 torque converter lever
35 gear-change (gearshift)
36 multi-speed transmission
37 fluid clutch (fluid drive)
38 power take-off gear
39 main clutch
40 power take-off gear-change
  (gearshift) with power take-off
  clutch
41 hydraulic power steering and
  reversing gears
42 fuel tank
43 float lever
44 four-cylinder diesel engine

45 oil sump and pump for the
  pressure-feed lubrication system
46 fresh oil tank
47 track rod (*Am.* tie rod)
48 front axle pivot pin
49 front axle suspension
50 front coupling (front hitch)
51 radiator
52 fan
53 battery
54 oil bath air cleaner (oil bath air
  filter)
55 **cultivator** (grubber)
56 sectional frame
57 spring tine
58 share, a diamond-shaped share;
  sim.: chisel-shaped share
59 depth wheel
60 depth adjustment
61 coupling (hitch)
62 **reversible plough** (*Am.* plow),
  a mounted plough
63 depth wheel
64-67 plough (*Am.* **plow) bottom,**
  a general-purpose plough bottom
64 mouldboard (*Am.* moldboard)
65 ploughshare (share, *Am.*
  plowshare), a pointed share
66 sole (slade)
67 landside
68 skim coulter (*Am.* colter)
69 disc (disk) coulter (*Am.* colter)
  (rolling coulter)
70 plough (*Am.* plow) frame
71 beam (plough beam, *Am.*
  plowbeam)
72 three-point linkage
73 swivel mechanism
74 **drill**
75 seed hopper
76 drill coulter (*Am.* colter)
77 delivery tube, a telescopic tube
78 feed mechanism
79 gearbox
80 drive wheel
81 track indicator
82 **disc (disk) harrow,**
  a semimounted implement
83 discs (disks) in X-configuration
84 plain disc (disk)
85 serrated-edge disc (disk)
86 quick hitch
87 **combination seed-harrow**
88 three-section spike-tooth
  harrow
89 three-section rotary harrow
90 frame

74

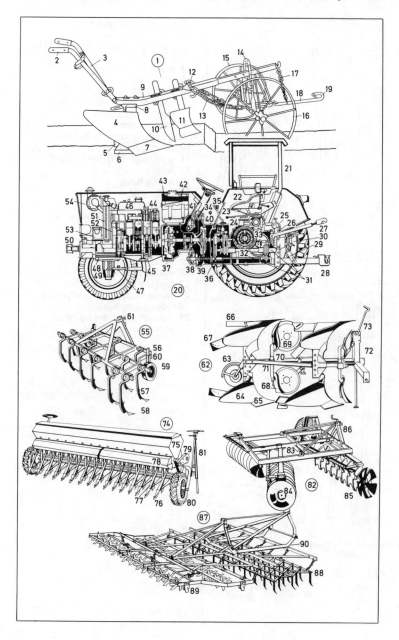

39 Agricultural Implements

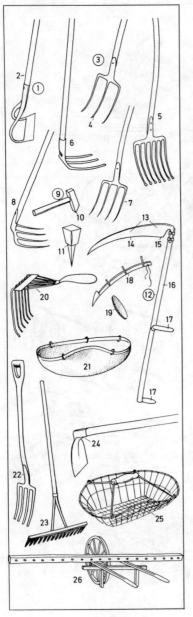

1 draw hoe (garden hoe)
2 hoe handle
3 three–pronged (three–tined) hay fork (fork)
4 prong (tine)
5 potato fork
6 potato hook
7 four–pronged (four–tined) manure fork (fork)
8 manure hoe
9 whetting hammer [for scythes]
10 peen (pane)
11 whetting anvil [for scythes]
12 scythe
13 scythe blade
14 cutting edge
15 heel
16 snath (snathe, snead, sneath)
17 handle
18 scythe sheath
19 whetstone (scythestone)
20 potato rake
21 potato planter
22 digging fork (fork)
23 wooden rake (rake, hayrake)
24 hoe (potato hoe)
25 potato basket, a wire basket
26 clover broadcaster

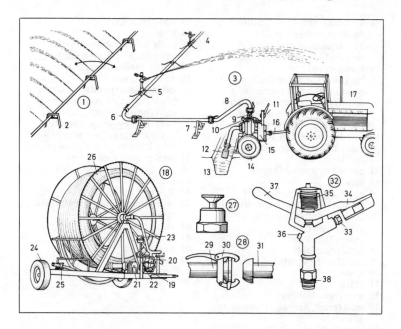

1 oscillating spray line
2 stand (steel chair)
3 portable irrigation system
4 revolving sprinkler
5 standpipe coupler
6 elbow with cardan joint (cardan coupling)
7 pipe support (trestle)
8 pump connection
9 delivery valve
10 pressure gauge (*Am.* gage) (manometer)
11 centrifugal evacuating pump
12 basket strainer
13 channel
14 chassis of the p.t.o.–driven pump (power take–off–driven pump)
15 p.t.o.–driven (power take–off–driven) pump
16 cardan shaft
17 tractor
18 long-range irrigation unit
19 drive connection
20 turbine
21 gearing (gears)

22 adjustable support
23 centrifugal evacuating pump
24 wheel
25 pipe support
26 polyester pipe
27 sprinkler nozzle
28 quick–fitting pipe connection with cardan joint
29 M–cardan
30 clamp
31 V–cardan
32 revolving sprinkler, a field sprinkler
33 nozzle
34 breaker
35 breaker spring
36 stopper
37 counterweight
38 thread

41 Arable Crops

1–47 arable crops (agricultural produce, farm produce)

1–37 varieties of grain (grain, cereals, farinaceous plants, bread–corn)

1 rye (*also:* corn, 'corn' often meaning the main cereal of a country or region; in Northern Germany: rye; in Southern Germany and Italy: wheat; in Sweden: barley; in Scotland: oats; in North America: maize; in China: rice)
2 ear of rye, a spike (head)
3 spikelet
4 ergot, a grain deformed by fungus [shown with mycelium]
5 corn stem after tillering
6 culm (stalk)
7 node of the culm
8 leaf (grain leaf)
9 leaf sheath (sheath)
10 spikelet
11 glume
12 awn (beard, arista)
13 seed (grain, kernel, farinaceous grain)
14 embryo plant
15 seed
16 embryo
17 root
18 root hair
19 grain leaf
20 leaf blade (blade, lamina)
21 leaf sheath
22 ligule (ligula)
23 wheat
24 spelt
25 seed; *unripe:* green spelt, a soup vegetable
26 barley
27 oat panicle, a panicle
28 millet
29 rice
30 rice grain
31 maize (Indian corn, *Am.* corn); *varieties:* popcorn, dent corn, flint corn (flint maize, *Am.* Yankee corn), pod corn (*Am.* cow corn, husk corn), soft corn (*Am.* flour corn, squaw corn), sweet corn
32 female inflorescence

33 husk (shuck)
34 style
35 male inflorescence (tassel)
36 maize cob (*Am.* corn cob)
37 maize kernel (grain of maize)

38–45 root crops

38 potato plant (potato), a tuberous plant; *varieties:* round, round–oval (pear–shaped), flat–oval, long, kidney–shaped potato; *according to colour:* white (*Am.* Irish), yellow, red, purple potato
39 seed potato (seed tuber)
40 potato tuber (potato, tuber)
41 potato top (potato haulm)
42 flower
43 poisonous potato berry (potato apple)
44 sugar beet, a beet
45 root (beet)
46 beet top
47 beet leaf

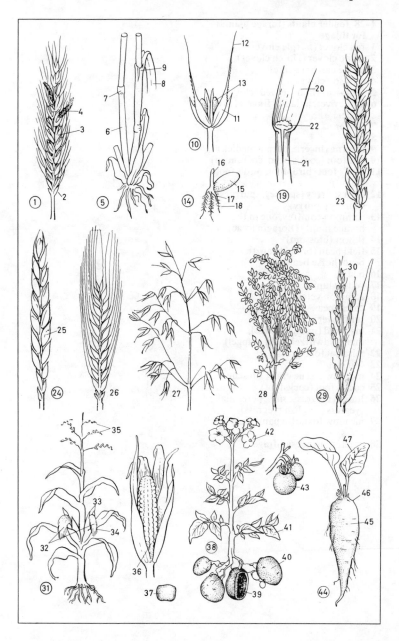

42 Fodder Plants (Forage Plants)

1-28 fodder plants (forage plants) for tillage

1 red clover (purple clover)
2 white clover (Dutch clover)
3 alsike clover (alsike)
4 crimson clover
5 four-leaf (four-leaved) clover
6 kidney vetch (lady's finger, lady-finger)
7 flower
8 pod
9 lucerne (lucern, purple medick)
10 sainfoin (cock's head, cockshead)
11 bird's foot (bird-foot, bird's foot trefoil)
12 corn spurrey (spurrey, spurry), a spurrey (spurry)
13 common comfrey, one of the borage family (Boraginaceae)
14 flower (blossom)
15 field bean (broad bean, tick bean, horse bean)
16 pod
17 yellow lupin
18 common vetch
19 chick-pea
20 sunflower
21 mangold (mangelwurzel, mangoldwurzel, field mangel)
22 false oat (oat-grass)
23 spikelet
24 meadow fescue grass, a fescue
25 cock's foot (cocksfoot)
26 Italian ryegrass; *sim.:* perennial ryegrass (English ryegrass)
27 meadow foxtail, a paniculate grass
28 greater burnet saxifrage

43 Breeds of Dog

1 bulldog
2 ear, a rose-ear
3 muzzle
4 nose
5 foreleg
6 forepaw
7 hind leg
8 hind paw
9 pug (pug dog)
10 boxer
11 withers
12 tail, a docked tail
13 collar
14 Great Dane
15 wire-haired fox terrier
16 bull terrier
17 Scottish terrier
18 Bedlington terrier
19 Pekinese (Pekingese, Pekinese dog, Pekingese dog)
20 spitz (Pomeranian)
21 chow (chow-chow)
22 husky

23 Afghan (Afghan hound)
24 greyhound (*Am.* grayhound), a courser
25 Alsatian (German sheepdog, *Am.* German shepherd), a police dog, watch dog, and guide dog
26 flews (chaps)
27 Dobermann terrier

28 dog brush
29 dog comb
30 lead (dog lead, leash); *for
   hunting:* leash
31 muzzle
32 feeding bowl (dog bowl)
33 bone
34 Newfoundland dog
35 schnauzer
36 poodle; *sim. and smaller:* pygmy
   (pigmy) poodle
37 St. Bernard (St. Bernard dog)
38 cocker spaniel
39 dachshund, a terrier
40 German pointer
41 English setter
42 trackhound
43 pointer, a trackhound

44 Horse I

1-6 **equitation** (high school riding, haute école)
1 piaffe
2 walk
3 passage
4 levade (pesade)
5 capriole
6 courbette (curvet)
7-25 **harness**
7-13 bridle
7-11 **headstall** (headpiece, halter)
7 noseband
8 cheek piece (cheek strap)
9 browband (front band)
10 crownpiece
11 throatlatch (throatlash)
12 curb chain
13 curb bit
14 hasp (hook) of the hame (*Am.* drag hook)
15 pointed collar, a collar
16 trappings (side trappings)
17 saddle-pad
18 girth
19 backband
20 shaft chain (pole chain)
21 pole
22 trace
23 second girth (emergency girth)
24 trace
25 reins (*Am.* lines)
26-36 **breast harness**
26 blinker (*Am.* blinder, winker)
27 breast collar ring
28 breast collar (Dutch collar)
29 fork
30 neck strap
31 saddle-pad
32 loin strap
33 reins (rein, *Am.* line)
34 crupper (crupper-strap)
35 trace
36 girth (belly-band)
37-49 **saddles**
37-44 **stock saddle** (*Am.* western saddle)
37 saddle seat
38 pommel horn (horn)
39 cantle
40 flap (*Am.* fender)
41 bar
42 stirrup leather

43 stirrup (stirrup iron)
44 blanket
45-49 **English saddle** (cavalry saddle)
45 seat
46 cantle
47 flap
48 roll (knee roll)
49 pad
50-51 **spurs**
50 box spur (screwed jack spur)
51 strapped jack spur
52 curb bit
53 gag bit (gag)
54 currycomb
55 horse brush (body brush, dandy brush)

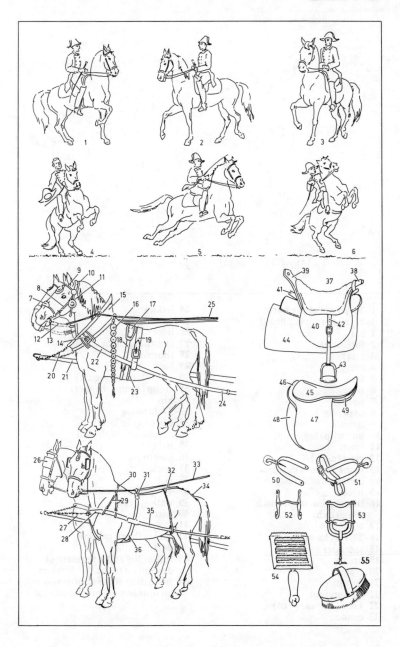

45 Horse II

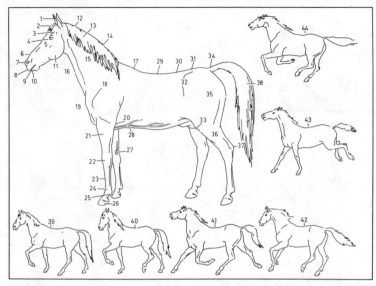

1–38 points of the horse
1–11 head (horse's head)
1 ear
2 forelock
3 forehead
4 eye
5 face
6 nose
7 nostril
8 upper lip
9 mouth
10 underlip (lower lip)
11 lower jaw
12 crest (neck)
13 mane (horse's mane)
14 crest (horse's crest)
15 neck
16 throat (*Am.* throatlatch, throatlash)
17 withers
18–27 forehand
18 shoulder
19 breast
20 elbow
21 forearm
22–26 forefoot
22 knee (carpus, wrist)
23 cannon

24 fetlock
25 pastern
26 hoof
27 chestnut (castor), a callosity
28 spur vein
29 back
30 loins (lumbar region)
31 croup (rump, crupper)
32 hip
33–37 hind leg
33 stifle (stifle joint)
34 root (dock) of the tail
35 haunch
36 gaskin
37 hock
38 tail
39–44 gaits of the horse
39 walk
40 pace
41 trot
42 canter (hand gallop)
43–44 full gallop
43 full gallop at the moment of descent on to the two forefeet
44 full gallop at the moment when all four feet are off the ground

Abbreviations:
- *m.* = male; *c.* = castrated; *f.* = female; *y.* = young

1–2 cattle
1 cow, a ruminant; *m.* bull; *c.* ox; *f.* cow; *y.* calf
2 horse; *m.* stallion; *c.* gelding; *f.* mare; *y.* foal
3 donkey
4 pack saddle (carrying saddle)
5 pack (load)
6 tufted tail
7 tuft
8 mule, a cross between a male donkey and a mare
9 pig, a cloven-hoofed animal; *m.* boar; *f.* sow; *y.* piglet
10 pig's snout (snout)
11 pig's ear
12 curly tail
13 sheep; *m.* ram; *c.* wether; *f.* ewe; *y.* lamb
14 goat
15 goat's beard
16 dog, a Leonberger; *m.* dog; *f.* bitch; *y.* pup (puppy, whelp)
17 cat, an Angora cat (Persian cat); *m.* tom (tom cat)

18–36 small domestic animals
18 rabbit; *m.* buck; *f.* doe
19–36 poultry (domestic fowl)
19–26 chicken
19 hen
20 crop (craw)
21 cock (*Am.* rooster); *c.* capon
22 cockscomb (comb, crest)
23 lap
24 wattle (gill, dewlap)
25 falcate (falcated) tail
26 spur
27 guinea fowl
28 turkey; *m.* turkey cock (gobbler); *f.* turkey hen
29 fan tail
30 peacock
31 peacock's feather
32 eye (ocellus)
33 pigeon; *m.* cock pigeon
34 goose; *m.* gander; *y.* gosling
35 duck; *m.* drake; *y.* duckling
36 web (palmations) of webbed foot (palmate foot)

47 Poultry Farming (Poultry Keeping), Egg Production

1–27 poultry farming (intensive poultry management)

1–17 straw yard (strawed yard) system

1 fold unit for growing stock (chick unit)
2 chick
3 brooder (hover)
4 adjustable feeding trough
5 pullet fold unit
6 drinking trough
7 water pipe
8 litter
9 pullet
10 ventilator

11–17 broiler rearing (rearing of broiler chickens)

11 chicken run (*Am.* fowl run)
12 broiler chicken (broiler)
13 mechanical feeder (self-feeder, feed dispenser)
14 chain
15 feed supply pipe
16 mechanical drinking bowl (mechanical drinker)
17 ventilator
18 battery system (cage system)
19 battery (laying battery)
20 tiered cage (battery cage, stepped cage)
21 feeding trough
22 egg collection by conveyor

23–27 mechanical feeding and dunging (manure removal, droppings removal)

23 rapid feeding system for battery feeding (mechanical feeder)
24 feed hopper
25 endless-chain conveyor (chain feeder)
26 water pipe (liquid feed pipe)
27 dunging chain (dunging conveyor)
28 [cabinet type] setting and hatching machine
29 ventilation drum [for the setting compartment]
30 hatching compartment (hatcher)
31 metal trolley for hatching trays
32 hatching tray
33 ventilation drum motor

34–53 egg production

34 egg collection system (egg collection)
35 multi-tier transport
36 collection by pivoted fingers
37 drive motor
38 sorting machine
39 conveyor trolley
40 fluorescent screen
41 suction apparatus (suction box) for transporting eggs
42 shelf for empty and full egg boxes
43 egg weighers
44 grading
45 egg box
46 fully automatic egg-packing machine
47 radioscope box
48 radioscope table

49–51 feeder

49 suction transporter
50 vacuum line
51 supply table
52 automatic counting and grading
53 packing box dispenser
54 leg ring
55 wing tally (identification tally)
56 bantam
57 laying hen
58 hen's egg (egg)
59 eggshell, an egg integument
60 shell membrane
61 air space
62 white [of the egg] (albumen)
63 chalaza (*Am.* treadle)
64 vitelline membrane (yolk sac)
65 blastodisc (germinal disc, cock's tread, cock's treadle)
66 germinal vesicle
67 white
68 yolk

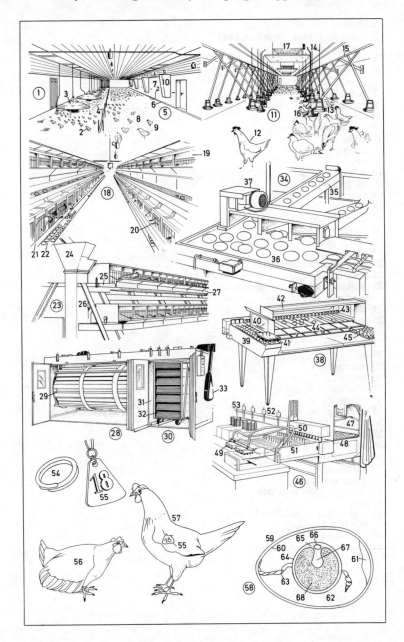

48 Rearing (*Am.* Raising) of Livestock

1 **stable**
2 horse stall (stall, horse box, box)
3 feeding passage
4 pony
5 bars
6 litter
7 bale of straw
8 ceiling light
9 **sheep pen**
10 mother sheep (ewe)
11 lamb
12 double hay rack
13 hay
14 **dairy cow shed**
15–16 tether
15 chain
16 rail
17 dairy cow (milch–cow, milker)
18 udder
19 teat
20 manure gutter
21 manure removal by sliding bars
22 short standing
23 **milking parlour** (*Am.* parlor), a
   herringbone parlour
24 working passage
25 milker (*Am.* milkman)
26 teat cup cluster
27 milk pipe
28 air line
29 vacuum line
30 teat cup
31 window
32 pulsator
33 release phase
34 squeeze phase
35 **pigsty** (*Am.* pigpen, hogpen)
36 pen for young pigs
37 feeding trough
38 partition
39 pig, a young pig
40 farrowing and store pen
41 sow
42 piglet (*Am.* shoat, shote) (sow pig
   [for first 8 weeks])
43 farrowing rails
44 liquid manure channel

49 Dairy

1-48 **dairy** (dairy plant)
1 **milk reception**
2 milk tanker
3 raw milk pump
4 flowmeter, an oval (elliptical) gear meter
5 raw milk storage tank
6 gauge (*Am.* gage)
7 **central control room**
8 chart of the dairy
9 flow chart (flow diagram)
10 storage tank gauges (*Am.* gages)
11 control panel
12-48 **milk processing area**
12 sterilizer (homogenizer)
13 milk heater; *sim.:* cream heater
14 cream separator
15 fresh milk tanks
16 tank for sterilized milk
17 skim milk (skimmed milk) tank
18 buttermilk tank
19 cream tank
20 fresh milk filling and packing plant
21 filling machine for milk cartons; *sim.:* milk tub filler
22 milk carton
23 conveyor belt (conveyor)
24 shrink-sealing machine
25 pack of twelve in shrink foil
26 ten-litre filling machine
27 heat-sealing machine
28 plastic sheets
29 heat-sealed bag
30 crate
31 cream maturing vat
32 butter shaping and packing machine
33 butter churn, a creamery butter machine for continuous butter making
34 butter supply pipe
35 shaping machine
36 packing machine
37 branded butter in 250 g packets
38 plant for producing curd cheese (curd cheese machine)
39 curd cheese pump
40 cream supply pump
41 curds separator
42 sour milk vat
43 stirrer
44 curd cheese packing machine
45 packeted curd cheese
46 bottle-capping machine (capper)
47 cheese machine
48 rennet vat

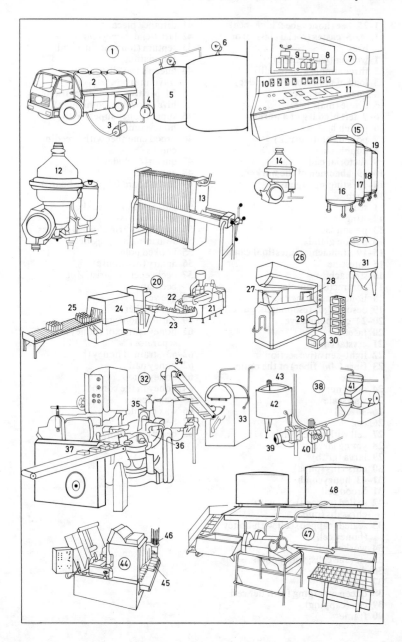

50 Bees and Beekeeping (Apiculture)

1-25 bee (honey-bee, hive-bee)
1, 4, 5 castes (social classes) of bees
1 worker (worker bee)
2 three simple eyes (ocelli)
3 load of pollen on the hind leg
4 queen (queen bee)
5 drone (male bee)
6-9 left hind leg of a worker
6 pollen basket
7 pollen comb (brush)
8 double claw
9 suctorial pad
10-19 abdomen of the worker
10-14 stinging organs
10 barb
11 sting
12 sting sheath
13 poison sac
14 poison gland
15-19 stomachic-intestinal canal
15 intestine
16 stomach
17 contractile muscle
18 honey bag (honey sac)
19 oesophagus (esophagus, gullet)
20-24 compound eye
20 facet
21 crystal cone
22 light-sensitive section
23 fibre (*Am.* fiber) of the optic nerve
24 optic nerve
25 wax scale
26-30 cell
26 egg
27 cell with the egg in it
28 young larva
29 larva (grub)
30 chrysalis (pupa)
31-43 honeycomb
31 brood cell
32 sealed (capped) cell with chrysalis (pupa)
33 sealed (capped) cell with honey (honey cell)
34 worker cells
35 storage cells, with pollen
36 drone cells
37 queen cell
38 queen emerging from her cell
39 cap (capping)
40 frame

41 distance piece
42 [artificial] honeycomb
43 septum (foundation, comb foundation)
44 queen's travelling (*Am.* traveling) box
45-50 beehive, a movable-frame hive (movable-comb hive)
45 super (honey super) with honeycombs
46 brood chamber with breeding combs
47 queen-excluder
48 entrance
49 flight board (alighting board)
50 window
51 old-fashioned bee shed
52 straw hive (skep), a hive
53 swarm (swarm cluster) of bees
54 swarming net (bag net)
55 hooked pole
56 apiary (bee house)
57 beekeeper (apiarist, *Am.* beeman)
58 bee veil
59 bee smoker
60 natural honeycomb
61 honey extractor (honey separator)
62-63 strained honey (honey)
62 honey pail
63 honey jar
64 honey in the comb
65 wax taper
66 wax candle
67 beeswax
68 bee sting ointment

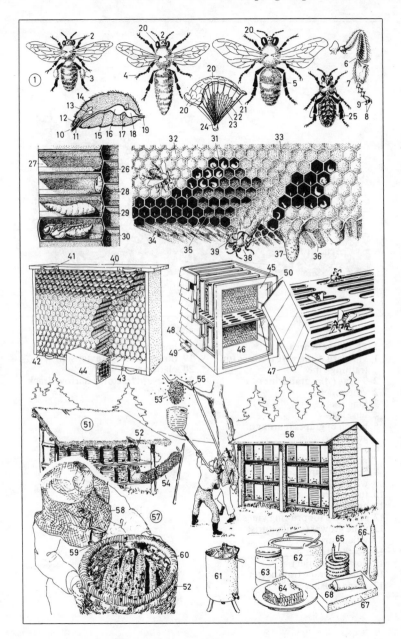

51 Wine Growing (Viniculture, Viticulture)

1–21 vineyard area
1 vineyard using wire trellises for training vines
2–9 vine (*Am.* grapevine)
2 vine shoot
3 long shoot
4 vine leaf
5 bunch of grapes (cluster of grapes)
6 vine stem
7 post (stake)
8 guy (guy wire)
9 wire trellis
10 tub for grape gathering
11 grape gatherer
12 secateurs for pruning vines
13 wine grower (viniculturist, viticulturist)
14 dosser carrier
15 dosser (pannier)
16 crushed grape transporter
17 grape crusher
18 hopper
19 three–sided flap extension
20 platform
21 vineyard tractor, a narrow–track tractor

1–22 wine cellar (wine vault)
1 vault
2 wine cask
3 wine vat, a concrete vat
4 stainless steel vat (*also:* vat made of synthetic material)
5 propeller–type high–speed mixer
6 propeller mixer
7 centrifugal pump
8 stainless steel sediment filter
9 semi–automatic circular bottling machine
10 semi–automatic corking machine
11 bottle rack
12 cellarer's assistant
13 bottle basket
14 wine bottle
15 wine jug
16 wine tasting
17 head cellarman
18 cellarman
19 wineglass

20 inspection apparatus [for spot–checking samples]
21 horizontal wine press
22 humidifier

53 Garden and Field Pests

1-19 fruit pests
1 gipsy (gypsy) moth
2 batch (cluster) of eggs
3 caterpillar
4 chrysalis (pupa)
5 small ermine moth, an ermine moth
6 larva (grub)
7 tent
8 caterpillar skeletonizing a leaf
9 fruit surface eating tortrix moth (summer fruit tortrix moth)
10 appleblossom weevil, a weevil
11 punctured, withered flower (blossom)
12 hole for laying eggs
13 lackey moth
14 caterpillar
15 eggs
16 winter moth, a geometrid
17 caterpillar
18 cherry fruit fly, a borer
19 larva (grub, maggot)

20-27 vine pests
20 downy mildew, a mildew, a disease causing leaf drop
21 grape affected with downy mildew
22 grape-berry moth
23 first-generation larva of the grape-berry moth (Am. grape worm)
24 second-generation larva of the grape-berry moth (Am. grape worm)
25 chrysalis (pupa)
26 root louse, a grape phylloxera
27 root gall (knotty swelling of the root, nodosity, tuberosity)
28 brown-tail moth
29 caterpillar
30 batch (cluster) of eggs
31 hibernation cocoon
32 woolly apple aphid (American blight), an aphid
33 gall caused by the woolly apple aphid
34 woolly apple aphid colony
35 San-José scale, a scale insect (scale louse)
36 larvae (grubs) [*male* elongated, *female* round]

37-55 field pests
37 click beetle, a snapping beetle (*Am.* snapping bug)
38 wireworm, larva of the click beetle
39 flea beetle
40 Hessian fly, a gall midge (gall gnat)
41 larva (grub)
42 turnip moth, an earth moth
43 chrysalis (pupa)
44 cutworm, a caterpillar
45 beet carrion beetle
46 larva (grub)
47 large cabbage white butterfly
48 caterpillar of the small cabbage white butterfly
49 brown leaf-eating weevil, a weevil
50 feeding site
51 sugar beet eelworm, a nematode (a threadworm, hairworm)
52 Colorado beetle (potato beetle)
53 mature larva (grub)
54 young larva (grub)
55 eggs

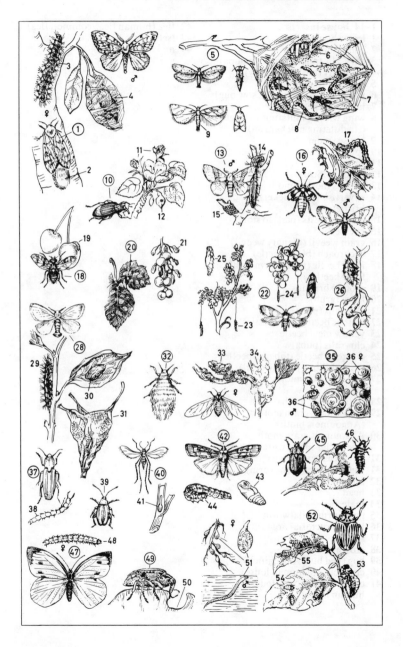

54 House Insects, Food Pests, and Parasites

1–14 house insects
1 lesser housefly
2 common housefly
3 chrysalis (pupa, coarctate pupa)
4 stable fly (biting housefly)
5 trichotomous antenna
6 wood louse (slater, *Am.* sow bug)
7 house cricket
8 wing with stridulating apparatus
  (stridulating mechanism)
9 house spider
10 spider's web
11 earwig
12 caudal pincers
13 clothes moth, a moth
14 silverfish (*Am.* slicker), a
  bristletail
15–30 food pests (pests to stores)
15 cheesefly
16 grain weevil (granary weevil)
17 cockroach (black beetle)
18 meal beetle (meal worm beetle,
  flour beetle)
19 spotted bruchus
20 larva (grub)
21 chrysalis (pupa)
22 leather beetle (hide beetle)
23 yellow meal beetle
24 chrysalis (pupa)
25 cigarette beetle (tobacco beetle)
26 maize billbug (corn weevil)
27 one of the Cryptolestes, a grain
  pest
28 Indian meal moth
29 Angoumois grain moth
  (Angoumois moth)
30 Angoumois grain moth
  caterpillar inside a grain kernel
31–42 parasites of man
31 round worm (maw worm)
32 female
33 head
34 male
35 tapeworm, a flatworm
36 head, a suctorial organ
37 sucker
38 crown of hooks
39 bug (bed bug, *Am.* chinch)
40 crab louse (a human louse)
41 clothes louse (body louse, a
  human louse)
42 flea (human flea, common flea)
43 tsetse fly
44 malaria mosquito

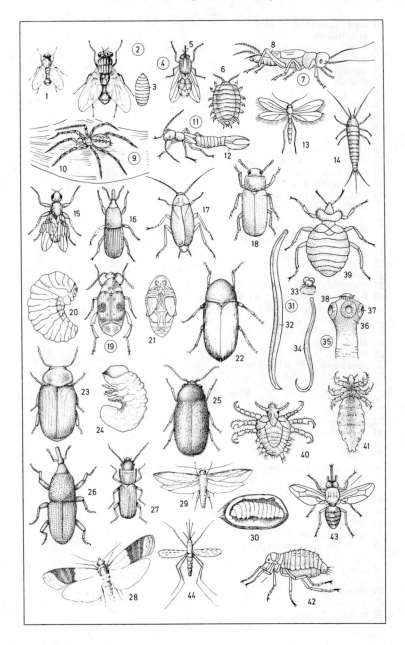

55 Forest Pests

1 cockchafer (May bug), a
  lamellicorn
2 head
3 antenna (feeler)
4 thoracic shield (prothorax)
5 scutellum
6-8 legs
6 front leg
7 middle leg
8 back leg
9 abdomen
10 elytron (wing case)
11 membranous wing
12 cockchafer grub, a larva
13 chrysalis (pupa)
14 processionary moth, a nocturnal
  moth (night-flying moth)
15 moth
16 caterpillars in procession
17 nun moth (black arches moth)
18 moth
19 eggs
20 caterpillar
21 chrysalis (pupa) in its cocoon
22 typographer beetle, a bark beetle
23-24 galleries under the bark
23 egg gallery
24 gallery made by larva
25 larva (grub)
26 beetle
27 pine hawkmoth, a hawkmoth
28 pine moth, a geometrid
29 male moth
30 female moth
31 caterpillar
32 chrysalis (pupa)
33 oak-gall wasp, a gall wasp
34 oak gall (oak apple), a gall
35 wasp
36 larva (grub) in its chamber
37 beech gall
38 spruce-gall aphid
39 winged aphid
40 pineapple gall
41 pine weevil
42 beetle (weevil)
43 green oak roller moth (green oak
  tortrix), a leaf roller
44 caterpillar
45 moth
46 pine beauty
47 caterpillar
48 moth

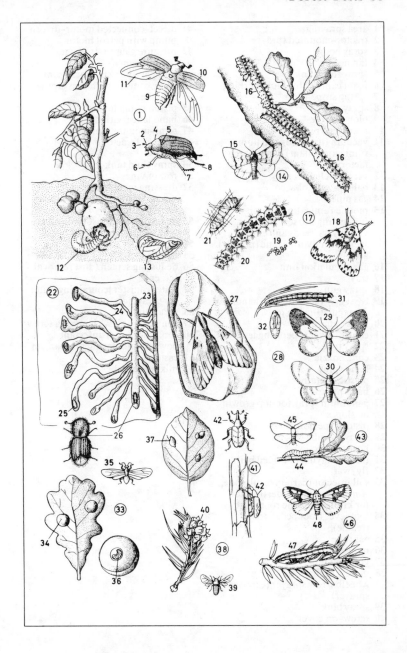

56 Pest Control

1 area spraying
2 tractor-mounted sprayer
3 spray boom
4 fan nozzle
5 spray fluid tank
6 foam canister for blob marking
7 spring suspension
8 spray
9 blob marker
10 foam feed pipe
11 vacuum fumigator (vacuum fumigation plant) of a tobacco factory
12 vacuum chamber
13 bales of raw tobacco
14 gas pipe
15 mobile fumigation chamber for fumigating nursery saplings, vine layers, seeds,and empty sacks with hydrocyanic (prussic) acid
16 gas circulation unit
17 tray
18 spray gun
19 twist grip (control grip, handle) for regulating the jet
20 finger guard
21 control lever (operating lever)
22 spray tube
23 cone nozzle
24 hand spray
25 plastic container
26 hand pump
27 pendulum spray for hop growing on slopes
28 pistol-type nozzle
29 spraying tube
30 hose connection
31 tube for laying poisoned bait
32 fly swat
33 soil injector (carbon disulphide, *Am.* carbon disulfide, injector) for killing the vine root louse
34 foot lever (foot pedal, foot treadle)
35 gas tube
36 mousetrap
37 vole and mole trap
38 mobile orchard sprayer, a wheelbarrow sprayer (carriage sprayer)
39 spray tank
40 screw-on cover

41 direct-connected motor-driven pump with petrol motor
42 pressure gauge (*Am.* gage) (manometer)
43 plunger-type knapsack sprayer
44 spray canister with pressure chamber
45 piston pump lever
46 hand lance with nozzle
47 semi-mounted sprayer
48 vineyard tractor
49 fan
50 spray fluid tank
51 row of vines
52 dressing machine (seed-dressing machine) for dry-seed dressing (seed dusting)
53 dedusting fan (dust removal fan) with electric motor
54 bag filter
55 bagging nozzle
56 dedusting screen (dust removal screen)
57 water canister [containing water for spraying]
58 spray unit
59 conveyor unit with mixing screw
60 container for disinfectant powder with dosing mechanism
61 castor
62 mixing chamber

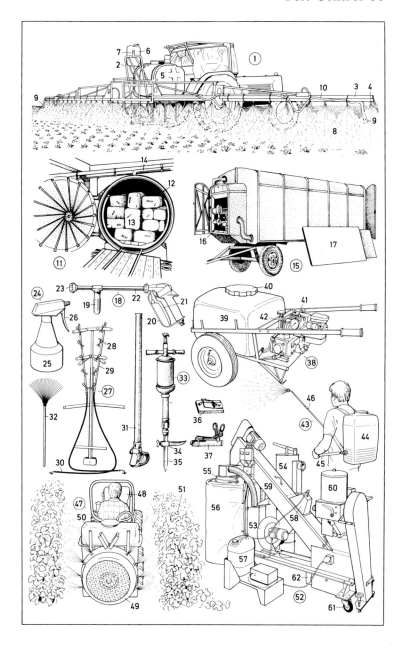

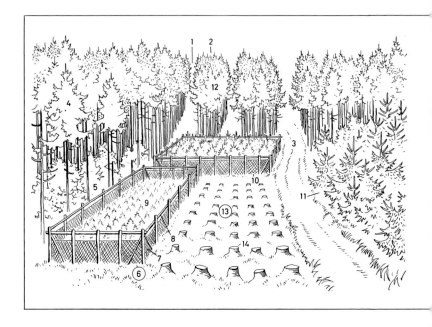

1-34 forest, a wood
1 ride (aisle, lane, section line)
2 compartment (section)
3 wood haulage way, a forest track
4-14 clear-felling system
4 standing timber
5 underwood (underbrush,
   undergrowth, brushwood, *Am.*
   brush)
6 seedling nursery, a tree nursery
7 deer fence (fence), a wire netting
   fence (protective fence for
   seedlings); *sim.:* rabbit fence
8 guard rail
9 seedlings
10-11 young trees
10 tree nursery after transplanting
11 young plantation
12 young plantation after brashing
13 clearing
14 tree stump (stump, stub)

15–37 wood cutting (timber cutting, tree felling, *Am.* lumbering)
15 timber skidded to the stack (stacked timber, *Am.* yarded timber)
16 stack of logs, one cubic metre (*Am.* meter) of wood
17 post (stake)
18 forest labourer (woodsman, *Am.* logger, lumberer, lumberjack, lumberman, timberjack) turning (*Am.* canting) timber
19 bole (tree trunk, trunk, stem)
20 feller numbering the logs
21 steel tree calliper (caliper)
22 power saw (motor saw) cutting a bole
23 safety helmet with visor and ear pieces
24 annual rings
25 hydraulic felling wedge
26 protective clothing [orange top, green trousers]
27 felling with a power saw (motor saw)

28 undercut (notch, throat, gullet, mouth, sink, kerf, birdsmouth)
29 back cut
30 sheath holding felling wedge
31 log
32 free-cutting saw for removing underwood and weeds
33 circular saw (or activated blade) attachment
34 power unit (motor)
35 canister of viscous oil for the saw chain
36 petrol canister (*Am.* gasoline canister)
37 felling of small timber (of small-sized thinnings) (thinning)

58 Forestry II

1 axe (*Am.* ax)
2 edge (cutting edge)
3 handle (helve)
4 felling wedge (falling wedge) with wood insert and ring
5 riving hammer (cleaving hammer, splitting hammer)
6 lifting hook
7 cant hook
8 barking iron (bark spud)
9 peavy
10 slide calliper (caliper) (calliper square)
11 billhook, a knife for lopping
12 revolving die hammer (marking hammer, marking iron, *Am.* marker)
13 power saw (motor saw)
14 saw chain
15 safety brake for the saw chain, with finger guard
16 saw guide
17 accelerator lock
18 snedding machine (trimming machine, *Am.* knotting machine, limbing machine)
19 feed rolls
20 flexible blade
21 hydraulic arm
22 trimming blade
23 debarking (barking, bark stripping) of boles
24 feed roller
25 cylinder trimmer
26 rotary cutter
27 short–haul skidder
28 loading crane
29 log grips
30 post
31 Ackermann steering system
32 log dump
33 number (identification number)
34 skidder
35 front blade (front plate)
36 crush–proof safety bonnet (*Am.* safety hood)
37 Ackermann steering system
38 cable winch
39 cable drum
40 rear blade (rear plate)
41 boles with butt ends held off the ground
42 haulage of timber by road

43 tractor (tractor unit)
44 loading crane
45 hydraulic jack
46 cable winch
47 post
48 bolster plate
49 rear bed (rear bunk)

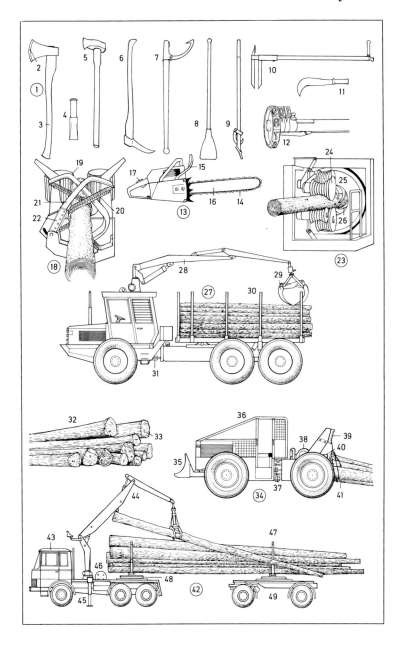

59 Colour (*Am.* Color)

1 red
2 yellow
3 blue
4 pink
5 brown
6 azure (sky blue)
7 orange
8 green
9 violet
10 additive mixture of colours (*Am.* colors)
11 white
12 subtractive mixture of colours (*Am.* colors)
13 black
14 solar spectrum (colours, *Am.* colors, of the rainbow)
15 grey (*Am.* gray) scale
16 heat colours (*Am.* colors)

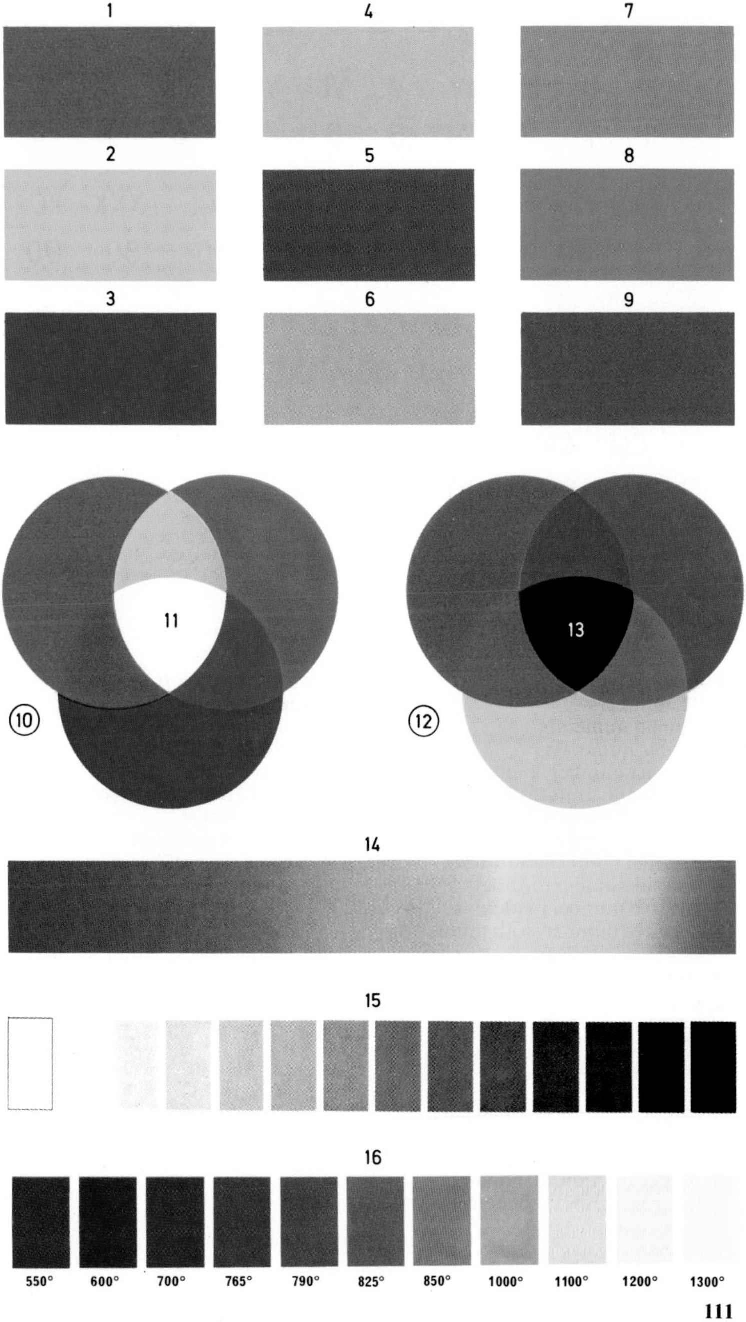

1
4
7
2
5
8
3
6
9

10
11

12
13

14

15

16

| 550° | 600° | 700° | 765° | 790° | 825° | 850° | 1000° | 1100° | 1200° | 1300° |

①	I	II	III	IV	V	VI	VII	VIII	IX	X
②	1	2	3	4	5	6	7	8	9	10

①	XX	XXX	XL	XLIX	IL	L	LX	LXX	LXXX	XC
②	20	30	40	49		50	60	70	80	90

①	XCIX	IC	C	CC	CCC	CD	D	DC	DCC	DCCC
②	99		100	200	300	400	500	600	700	800

①	CM	CMXC	M
②	900	990	1000

③ 9658   ④ 5 kg.   ⑤ 2   ⑥ 2nd   ⑦ +5   ⑧ -5

1–26 arithmetic
1–22 numbers
1 Roman numerals
2 Arabic numerals
3 abstract number, a four–figure number [8: units; 5: tens; 6: hundreds; 9: thousands]
4 concrete number
5 cardinal number (cardinal)
6 ordinal number (ordinal)
7 positive number [with plus sign]
8 negative number [with minus sign]
9 algebraic symbols
10 mixed number [3: whole number (integer); $\frac{1}{3}$: fraction]
11 even numbers
12 odd numbers
13 prime numbers
14 complex number [3: real part; $2\sqrt{-1}$: imaginary part]
15–16 vulgar fractions
15 proper fraction [2: numerator, horizontal line; 3: denominator]

16 improper fraction, also the reciprocal of item 15
17 compound fraction (complex fraction)
18 improper fraction [when cancelled down produces a whole number]
19 fractions of different denominations [35: common denominator]
20 proper decimal fraction with decimal point and decimal places [3: tenths; 5: hundredths; 7: thousandths]
21 recurring decimal
22 recurring decimal

⑨ **a, b, c ...** ⑩ $3\frac{1}{3}$ ⑪ **2, 4, 6, 8** ⑫ **1, 3, 5, 7**

⑬ **3, 5, 7, 11** ⑭ $3 + 2\sqrt{-1}$ ⑮ $\frac{2}{3}$ ⑯ $\frac{3}{2}$

⑰ $\dfrac{\frac{5}{6}}{\frac{3}{4}}$ ⑱ $\frac{12}{4}$ ⑲ $\frac{4}{5} + \frac{2}{7} = \frac{38}{35}$ ⑳ **0·357**

㉑ $0·6666.... = 0·\overline{6}$ ㉒ ㉓ **3 + 2 = 5**

㉔ **3 − 2 = 1** ㉕ **3 · 2 = 6** ㉖ **6 ÷ 2 = 3**
　　　　　　　　　　　3 × 2 = 6

23–26 fundamental arithmetical operations

23 addition (adding) [3 and 2: the terms of the sum; +: plus sign; =: equals sign; 5: the sum]

24 subtraction (subtracting); [3: the minuend; − : minus sign; 2: the subtrahend; 1: the remainder (difference)]

25 multiplication (multiplying); [3: the multiplicand; ×: multiplication sign; 2: the multiplier; 2 and 3: factors; 6: the product]

26 division (dividing); [6: the dividend; ÷: division sign; 2: the divisor; 3: the quotient]

① $3^2 = 9$ ② $\sqrt[3]{8} = 2$ ③ $\sqrt{4} = 2$

④ $3x + 2 = 12$

⑥

⑤ $4a + 6ab - 2ac = 2a(2 + 3b - c)$ $\log_{10} 3 = 0{\cdot}4771$

⑦ $\dfrac{P[\pounds 1000] \times R[5\%] \times T[2\,\text{years}]}{100} = I[\pounds 100]$

1-24 arithmetic
1-10 advanced arithmetical operations
1 raising to a power [three squared (3^2): the power; 3: the base; 2: the exponent (index); 9: value of the power]
2 evolution (extracting a root); [cube-root of 8: cube root; 8: the radical; 3: the index (degree) of the root; $\sqrt{\ }$: radical sign; 2: value of the root]
3 square root
4-5 algebra
4 simple equation [3, 2: the coefficients; x: the unknown quantity]
5 identical equation; [a, b, c: algebraic symbols]
6 logarithmic calculation (taking the logarithm, log); [log: logarithm sign; 3: number whose logarithm is required; 10: the base; 0: the characteristic; 4771: the mantissa; 0.4771: the logarithm]
7 simple interest formula; [P: the principal; R: rate of interest; T: time; I: interest (profit); %: percentage sign]
8-10 rule of three (rule-of-three sum, simple proportion)
8 statement with the unknown quantity x
9 equation (conditional equation)
10 solution
11-14 higher mathematics
11 arithmetical series with the elements 2, 4, 6, 8
12 geometrical series
13-14 infinitesimal calculus
13 derivative [dx, dy: the differentials; d: differential sign]
14 integral (integration); [x: the variable; C: constant of integration; S: the integral sign; dx: the differential]

⑧ 2 years @ £ 50
4 years @ £ x
———————————
⑨ 2 : 50 = 4 : x
⑩ x = £ 100

⑪ 2 + 4 + 6 + 8 ....

⑫ 2 + 4 + 8 + 16 + 32 ....

⑬ $\dfrac{dy}{dx}$

⑭ $\int a x\, dx = a \int x\, dx = \dfrac{a x^2}{2} + C$

⑮ ∞   ⑯ ≡   ⑰ ≈   ⑱ ≠   ⑲ >

⑳ <   ㉑ ∥   ㉒ ~   ㉓ ∢   ㉔ △

15–24 mathematical symbols
15 infinity
16 identically equal to (the sign of identity)
17 approximately equal to
18 unequal to
19 greater than
20 less than
21–24 geometrical symbols
21 parallel (sign of parallelism)
22 similar to (sign of similarity)
23 angle symbol
24 triangle symbol

62 Mathematics III (Geometry I)

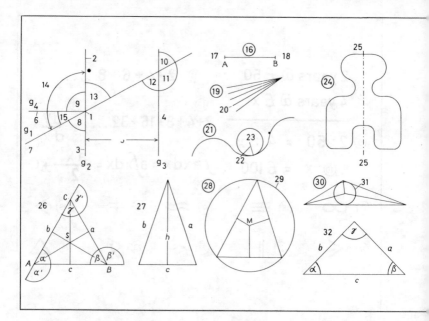

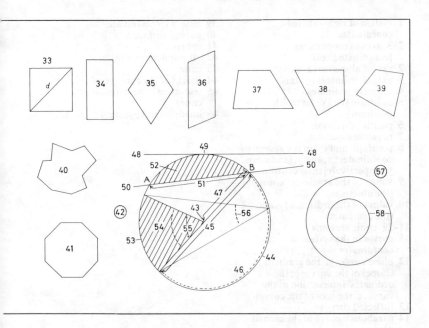

30 obtuse–angled triangle with bisectors of the angles
31 inscribed circle
32 right–angled triangle and the trigonometrical functions of angles; [a, b: the catheti; c: the hypotenuse; γ: the right angle; $\frac{a}{c} = \sin \alpha$ (sine); $\frac{b}{c} = \cos \alpha$ (cosine: $\frac{a}{b} = \tan \alpha$ (tangent); $\frac{b}{a} = \cot \alpha$ (cotangent)]
33–39 quadrilaterals
33–36 parallelograms
33 square [d: a diagonal]
34 rectangle
35 rhombus (rhomb, lozenge)
36 rhomboid
37 trapezium
38 deltoid (kite)
39 irregular quadrilateral
40 polygon
41 regular polygon
42 circle
43 centre (*Am.* center)
44 circumference (periphery)
45 diameter

46 semicircle
47 radius (r)
48 tangent
49 point of contact (P)
50 secant
51 the chord AB
52 segment
53 arc
54 sector
55 angle subtended by the arc at the centre (*Am.* center) (centre, *Am.* center, angle)
56 circumferential angle
57 ring (annulus)
58 concentric circles

63 Mathematics IV (Geometry II)

1 **system of right-angled coordinates**
2–3 axes of coordinates (coordinate axes)
2 axis of abscissae (x-axis)
3 axis of ordinates (y-axis)
4 origin of ordinates
5 quadrant [I – IV: 1st to 4th quadrant]
6 positive direction
7 negative direction
8 points [P_1 and P_2] in the system of coordinates; x_1 and y_1 [and x_2 and y_2 respectively] their coordinates
9 values of the abscissae [x_1 and x_2] (the abscissae)
10 values of the ordinates [y_1 and y_2] (the ordinates)
11–29 **conic sections**
11 **curves in the system of coordinates**
12 plane curves [a: the gradient (slope) of the curve; b: the ordinates' intersection of the curve; c: the root of the curve]
13 inflected curves
14 **parabola**, a curve of the second degree
15 branches of the parabola
16 vertex of the parabola
17 axis of the parabola
18 **a curve of the third degree**
19 maximum of the curve
20 minimum of the curve
21 point of inflexion (of inflection)
22 **ellipse**
23 transverse axis (major axis)
24 conjugate axis (minor axis)
25 foci of the ellipse [F_1 and F_2]
26 **hyperbola**
27 foci [F_1 and F_2]
28 vertices [S_1 and S_2]
29 asymptotes [a and b]
30–46 **solids**
30 cube
31 square, a plane (plane surface)
32 edge
33 corner
34 quadratic prism
35 base
36 parallelepiped
37 triangular prism
38 cylinder, a right cylinder

39 base, a circular plane
40 curved surface
41 sphere
42 ellipsoid of revolution
43 cone
44 height of the cone (cone height)
45 truncated cone (frustum of a cone)
46 quadrilateral pyramid

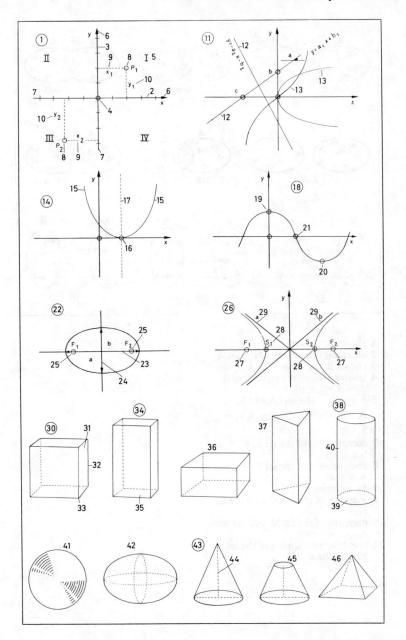

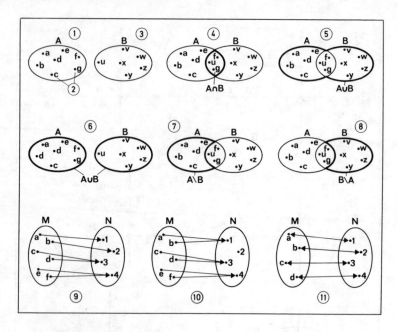

1 the set A, the set{a, b, c, d, e, f, g}
2 elements (members) of the set A
3 the set B, the set {u, v, w, x, y, z}
4 intersection of the sets A and B,
  A ∩ B ={f, g, u}
5–6 union of the sets A and B,
  A ∪ B ={a, b, c, d, e, f, g, u, v, w, x, y, z}
7 complement of the set B, B′ ={a, b, c, d, e}
8 complement of the set A, A′ ={v, w, x, y, z}
9–11 mappings
9 mapping of the set M *onto* the set N
10 mapping of the set M *into* the set N
11 one-to-one mapping of the set M onto the set N

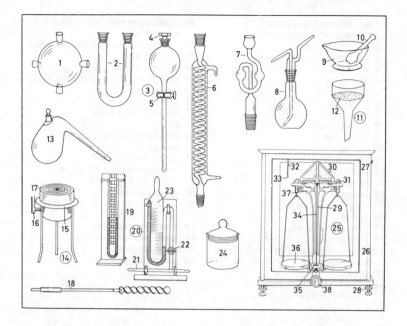

1-38 laboratory apparatus
(laboratory equipment)
1 Scheidt globe
2 U-tube
3 separating funnel
4 octagonal ground-glass stopper
5 tap (*Am.* faucet)
6 coiled condenser
7 air lock
8 wash-bottle
9 mortar
10 pestle
11 filter funnel (Büchner funnel)
12 filter (filter plate)
13 retort
14 water bath
15 tripod
16 water gauge (*Am.* gage)
17 insertion rings
18 stirrer
19 manometer for measuring
positive and negative pressures
20 mirror manometer for
measuring small pressures

21 inlet
22 tap (*Am.* faucet)
23 sliding scale
24 weighing bottle
25 analytical balance
26 case
27 sliding front panel
28 three-point support
29 column (balance column)
30 balance beam (beam)
31 rider bar
32 rider holder
33 rider
34 pointer
35 scale
36 scale pan
37 stop
38 stop knob

66 Chemistry Laboratory II

1–63 laboratory apparatus
(laboratory equipment)
1 Bunsen burner
2 gas inlet (gas inlet pipe)
3 air regulator
4 Teclu burner
5 pipe union
6 gas regulator
7 stem
8 air regulator
9 bench torch
10 casing
11 oxygen inlet
12 hydrogen inlet
13 oxygen jet
14 tripod
15 ring (retort ring)
16 funnel
17 pipe clay triangle
18 wire gauze
19 wire gauze with asbestos centre
   (*Am.* center)
20 beaker
21 burette (for measuring the
   volume of liquids)
22 burette stand
23 burette clamp
24 graduated pipette
25 pipette
26 measuring cylinder (measuring
   glass)
27 measuring flask
28 volumetric flask
29 evaporating dish (evaporating
   basin), made of porcelain
30 tube clamp (tube clip,
   pinchcock)
31 clay crucible with lid
32 crucible tongs
33 clamp
34 test tube
35 test tube rack
36 flat-bottomed flask
37 ground glass neck
38 long-necked round-bottomed
   flask
39 Erlenmeyer flask (conical flask)
40 filter flask
41 fluted filter
42 one-way tap
43 calcium chloride tube
44 stopper with tap
45 cylinder

46 distillation apparatus (distilling
   apparatus)
47 distillation flask (distilling flask)
48 condenser
49 return tap, a two-way tap
50 distillation flask (distilling flask,
   Claisen flask)
51 desiccator
52 lid with fitted tube
53 tap
54 desiccator insert made of
   porcelain
55 three-necked flask
56 connecting piece (Y-tube)
57 three-necked bottle
58 gas-washing bottle
59 gas generator (Kipp's apparatus,
   Am. Kipp generator)
60 overflow container
61 container for the solid
62 acid container
63 gas outlet

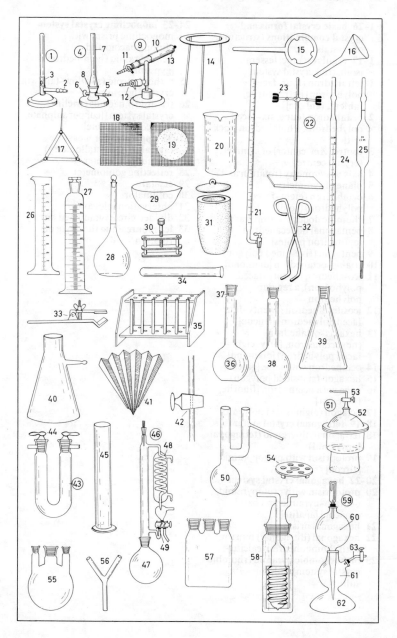

67 Crystals, Crystallography

1–26 basic crystal forms and crystal combinations (structure of crystals)

1–17 regular (cubic, tesseral, isometric) crystal system

1 tetrahedron (four–faced polyhedron) [tetrahedrite, fahlerz, fahl ore]
2 hexahedron (cube, six–faced polyhedron), a holohedron [rock salt]
3 centre (*Am.* center) of symmetry (crystal centre)
4 axis of symmetry (rotation axis)
5 plane of symmetry
6 octahedron (eight–faced polyhedron) [gold]
7 rhombic dodecahedron [garnet]
8 pentagonal dodecahedron [pyrite, iron pyrites]
9 pentagon (five–sided polygon)
10 triakis–octahedron [diamond]
11 icosahedron (twenty–faced polyhedron), a regular polyhedron
12 icositetrahedron (twenty–four-faced polyhedron) [leucite]
13 hexakis–octahedron (hexoctahedron, forty–eight-faced polyhedron) [diamond]
14 octahedron with cube [galena]
15 hexagon (six–sided polygon)
16 cube with octahedron [fluorite, fluorspar]
17 octagon (eight–sided polygon)

18–19 tetragonal crystal system

18 tetragonal dipyramid (tetragonal bipyramid)
19 protoprism with protopyramid [zircon]

20–22 hexagonal crystal system

20 protoprism with protopyramid, deutero–pyramid and basal pinacoid [apatite]
21 hexagonal prism
22 hexagonal (ditrigonal) biprism with rhombohedron [calcite]
23 orthorhombic pyramid (rhombic crystal system) [sulphur, *Am.* sulfur]

24–25 monoclinic crystal system

24 monoclinic prism with clinoprinacoid and hemipyramid (hemihedron) [gypsum]
25 orthopinacoid (swallow–tail twin crystal) [gypsum]
26 triclinic pinacoids (triclinic crystal system) [copper sulphate, *Am.* copper sulfate]

27–33 apparatus for measuring crystals (for crystallometry)

27 contact goniometer
28 reflecting goniometer
29 crystal
30 collimator
31 observation telescope
32 divided circle (graduated circle)
33 lens for reading the angle of rotation

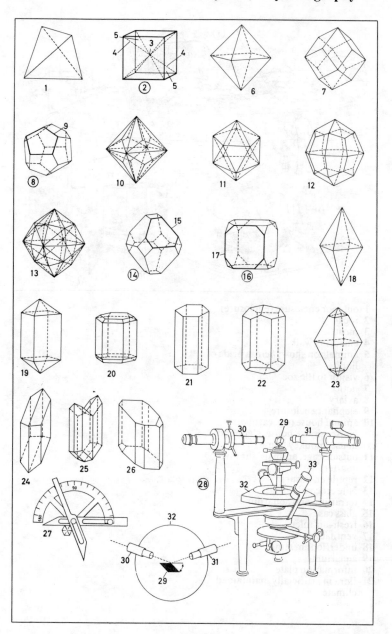

68 Zoo (Zoological Gardens)

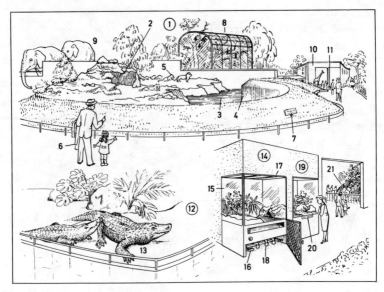

1 outdoor enclosure (enclosure)
2 rocks
3 moat
4 enclosing wall
5 animals on show; *here:* a pride of lions
6 visitor to the zoo
7 notice
8 aviary
9 elephant enclosure
10 animal house (e.g. carnivore house, giraffe house, elephant house, monkey house)
11 outside cage, animals' summer quarters
12 reptile enclosure
13 Nile crocodile
14 terrarium and aquarium
15 glass case
16 fresh–air inlet
17 ventilator
18 underfloor heating
19 aquarium
20 information plate
21 flora in artificially maintained climate

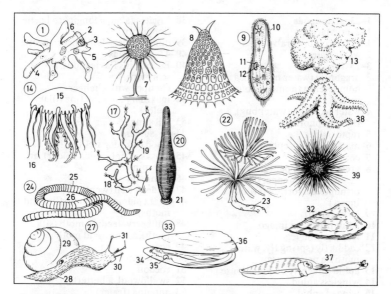

1-12 unicellular (one-celled, single-celled) animals (protozoans)
1 amoeba, a rhizopod
2 cell nucleus
3 protoplasm
4 pseudopod
5 excretory vacuole (contractile vacuole, an organelle)
6 food vacuole
7 Actinophrys, a heliozoan
8 radiolarian; *here:* siliceous skeleton
9 slipper animalcule, a Paramecium
10 cilium
11 macronucleus (meganucleus)
12 micronucleus
13-39 multicellular animals (metazoans)
13 bath sponge, a porifer (sponge)
14 medusa, a discomedusa (jellyfish), a coelenterate
15 umbrella
16 tentacle
17 red coral (precious coral), a coral animal (anthozoan, reef-building animal)

18 coral colony
19 coral polyp
20-26 worms (Vermes)
20 leech, an annelid
21 sucker
22 Spirographis, a bristle worm
23 tube
24 earthworm
25 segment
26 clitellum [accessory reproductive organ]
27-36 molluscs (*Am.* mollusks; *also:* testaceans and crustaceans)
27 edible snail, a snail
28 creeping foot
29 shell (snail shell)
30 stalked eye
31 tentacle (horn, feeler)
32 oyster
33 freshwater pearl mussel
34 mother-of-pearl (nacre)
35 pearl
36 mussel shell
37 cuttlefish, a cephalopod
38-39 echinoderms
38 starfish (sea star)
39 sea urchin (sea hedgehog)

70 Articulates

1–23 **arthropods**
1–2 **crustaceans**
1 mitten crab, a crab
2 water slater
3–23 **insects**
3 dragonfly (water nymph), a homopteran (homopterous insect)
4 water scorpion (water bug), a rhynchophore
5 raptorial leg
6 mayfly (dayfly, ephemerid)
7 compound eye
8 green grasshopper (green locust, meadow grasshopper), an orthopteron (orthopterous insect)
9 larva (grub)
10 adult insect, an imago
11 leaping hind leg
12 caddis fly (spring fly, water moth), a neuropteran
13 aphid (greenfly), a plant louse
14 wingless aphid
15 winged aphid
16–20 **dipterous insects** (dipterans)
16 gnat (mosquito, midge), a culicid
17 proboscis (sucking organ)
18 bluebottle (blowfly), a fly
19 maggot (larva)
20 chrysalis (pupa)
21–23 **Hymenoptera**
21–22 ant
21 winged female
22 worker
23 bumblebee (humblebee)
24–39 **beetles** (Coleoptera)
24 stag beetle, a lamellicorn beetle
25 mandibles
26 trophi
27 antenna (feeler)
28 head
29–30 thorax
29 thoracic shield (prothorax)
30 scutellum
31 tergites
32 stigma
33 wing (hind wing)
34 nervure
35 point at which the wing folds
36 elytron (forewing)
37 ladybird (ladybug), a coccinellid

38 Ergates faber, a longicorn beetle (longicorn)
39 dung beetle, a lamellicorn beetle
40–47 **arachnids**
40 Euscorpius flavicandus, a scorpion
41 cheliped with chelicer
42 maxillary antenna (maxillary feeler)
43 tail sting
44–46 **spiders**
44 wood tick (dog tick), a tick
45 cross spider (garden spider), an orb spinner
46 spinneret
47 spider's web (web)
48–56 **Lepidoptera** (butterflies and moths)
48 mulberry-feeding moth (silk moth), a bombycid moth
49 eggs
50 silkworm
51 cocoon
52 swallowtail, a butterfly
53 antenna (feeler)
54 eyespot
55 privet hawkmoth, a hawkmoth (sphinx)
56 proboscis

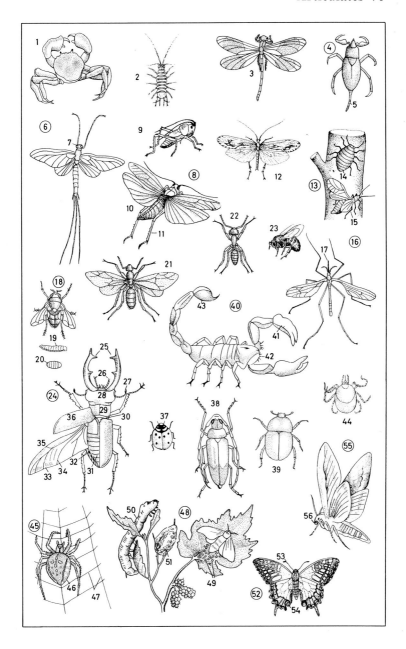

71 Birds I

1-3 flightless birds
1 cassowary; *sim.:* emu
2 ostrich
3 clutch of ostrich eggs [12 – 14 eggs]
4 king penguin, a penguin, a flightless bird
5-10 web-footed birds
5 white pelican, a pelican
6 webfoot (webbed foot)
7 web (palmations) of webbed foot (palmate foot)
8 lower mandible with gular pouch
9 northern gannet (gannet, solan goose), a gannet
10 green cormorant (shag), a cormorant displaying with spread wings
11-14 long-winged birds (seabirds)
11 common sea swallow, a sea swallow (tern); diving for food
12 fulmar
13 guillemot, an auk
14 black-headed gull (mire crow), a gull
15-17 Anseres
15 goosander (common merganser), a sawbill
16 mute swan, a swan
17 knob on the bill
18 common heron, a heron
19-21 plovers
19 stilt (stilt bird, stilt plover)
20 coot, a rail
21 lapwing (green plover, peewit, pewit)
22 quail, a gallinaceous bird
23 turtle dove, a pigeon
24 swift
25 hoopoe, a roller
26 erectile crest
27 spotted woodpecker, a woodpecker; *related:* wryneck
28 entrance to the nest
29 nesting cavity
30 cuckoo

72 Birds II (European Birds)

1, 3, 4, 5, 7, 9, 10 songbirds
1 goldfinch, a finch
2 bee eater
3 redstart (star finch), a thrush
4 bluetit, a tit (titmouse), a resident
   bird (non-migratory bird)
5 bullfinch
6 common roller (roller)
7 golden oriole, a migratory bird
8 kingfisher
9 white wagtail, a wagtail
10 chaffinch

73 Birds III (Passerines)

1–20 songbirds
1–3 Corvidae (corvine birds, crows)
1 jay (nutcracker)
2 rook, a crow
3 magpie
4 starling (pastor, shepherd bird)
5 house sparrow
6–8 finches
6–7 buntings
6 yellowhammer (yellow bunting)
7 ortolan (ortolan bunting)
8 siskin (aberdevine)
9 great titmouse (great tit, ox eye), a titmouse (tit)
10 golden–crested wren (goldcrest); *sim.:* firecrest, one of the Regulidae
11 nuthatch
12 wren
13–17 thrushes
13 blackbird
14 nightingale (*poet.:* philomel, philomela)

15 robin (redbreast, robin redbreast)
16 song thrush (throstle, mavis)
17 thrush nightingale
18–19 larks
18 woodlark
19 crested lark (tufted lark)
20 common swallow (barn swallow, chimney swallow), a swallow

1–13 diurnal birds of prey
1–4 falcons
1 merlin
2 peregrine falcon
3 leg feathers
4 tarsus
5–9 eagles
5 white–tailed sea eagle (white-tailed eagle, grey sea eagle, erne)
6 hooked beak
7 claw (talon)
8 tail
9 common buzzard
10–13 accipiters
10 goshawk
11 common European kite (glede, kite)
12 sparrow hawk (spar-hawk)
13 marsh harrier (moor buzzard, moor harrier, moor hawk)
14–19 owls (nocturnal birds of prey)
14 long–eared owl (horned owl)
15 eagle–owl (great horned owl)
16 plumicorn (feathered ear, ear tuft, ear, horn)

17 barn owl (white owl, silver owl, yellow owl, church owl, screech owl)
18 facial disc (disk)
19 little owl (sparrow owl)

75 Birds V (Exotic Birds)

1 sulphur–crested cockatoo, a
  parrot
2 blue–and–yellow macaw
3 blue bird of paradise
4 sappho
5 cardinal (cardinal bird)
6 toucan (red–billed toucan), one
  of the Piciformes

76 Fish, Amphibia, and Reptiles

1–18 fishes
1 man-eater (blue shark, requin), a shark
2 nose (snout)
3 gill slit (gill cleft)
4 mirror carp, a carp
5 gill cover (operculum)
6 dorsal fin
7 pectoral fin
8 pelvic fin (abdominal fin, ventral fin)
9 anal fin
10 caudal fin (tail fin)
11 scale
12 catfish (sheatfish, sheathfish, wels)
13 barbel
14 herring
15 brown trout, a trout
16 pike (northern pike)
17 freshwater eel (eel)
18 sea horse (Hippocampus, horsefish)
19 tufted gills
20–26 Amphibia (amphibians)
20–22 salamanders
20 greater water newt (crested newt), a water newt
21 dorsal crest
22 fire salamander, a salamander
23–26 salientians (anurans, batrachians)
23 European toad, a toad
24 tree frog (tree toad)
25 vocal sac (vocal pouch, croaking sac)
26 adhesive disc (disk)
27–41 reptiles
27, 30–37 lizards
27 sand lizard
28 hawksbill turtle (hawksbill)
29 carapace (shell)
30 basilisk
31 desert monitor, a monitor lizard (monitor)
32 common iguana, an iguana
33 chameleon, one of the Chamaeleontidae (Rhiptoglossa)
34 prehensile foot
35 prehensile tail
36 wall gecko, a gecko
37 slowworm (blindworm), one of the Anguidae

38–41 snakes
38 ringed snake (ring snake, water snake, grass snake), a colubrid
39 collar
40–41 vipers (adders)
40 common viper, a poisonous (venomous) snake
41 asp (asp viper)

77 Lepidoptera (Butterflies and Moths)

1-6 butterflies
1 red admiral
2 peacock butterfly
3 orange tip (orange tip butterfly)
4 brimstone (brimstone butterfly)
5 Camberwell beauty (mourning
   cloak, mourning cloak butterfly)
6 blue (lycaenid butterfly,
   lycaenid)
7-11 moths (Heterocera)
7 garden tiger
8 red underwing
9 death's-head moth (death's-
   head hawkmoth), a hawkmoth
   (sphinx)
10 caterpillar
11 chrysalis (pupa)

78 Mammals I

1 platypus (duck-bill, duck-mole),
a monotreme (oviparous
mammal)
2-3 marsupial mammals
(marsupials)
2 New World opossum, a didelphid
3 red kangaroo (red flyer), a
kangaroo
4-7 insectivores (insect-eating
mammals)
4 mole
5 hedgehog
6 spine
7 shrew (shrew mouse), one of the
Soricidae
8 nine-banded armadillo (peba)
9 long-eared bat (flitter-mouse), a
flying mammal (chiropter,
chiropteran)
10 pangolin (scaly ant-eater), a
scaly mammal
11 two-toed sloth (unau)
12-19 rodents
12 guinea pig (cavy)
13 porcupine
14 beaver
15 jerboa
16 hamster
17 water vole
18 marmot
19 squirrel
20 African elephant, a
proboscidean (proboscidian)
21 trunk (proboscis)
22 tusk
23 manatee (manati, lamantin), a
sirenian
24 South African dassie (das, coney,
hyrax), a procaviid
25-31 ungulates
25-27 odd-toed ungulates
25 African black rhino, a
rhinoceros (nasicorn)
26 Brazilian tapir, a tapir
27 zebra
28-31 even-toed ungulates
28-30 ruminants
28 llama
29 Bactrian camel (two-humped
camel)
30 guanaco
31 hippopotamus

79 Mammals II

1–10 ungulates, ruminants
1–10
1 elk (moose)
2 wapiti (*Am*. elk)
3 chamois
4 giraffe
5 black buck, an antelope
6 mouflon (moufflon)
7 ibex (rock goat, bouquetin, steinbock)
8 water buffalo (Indian buffalo, water ox)
9 bison
10 musk ox
11–22 carnivores (beasts of prey)
11–13 Canidae
11 black–backed jackal (jackal)
12 red fox
13 wolf
14–17 martens
14 stone marten (beach marten)
15 sable
16 weasel
17 sea otter, an otter
18–22 seals (pinnipeds)
18 fur seal (sea bear, ursine seal)
19 common seal (sea calf, sea dog)
20 walrus (morse)
21 whiskers
22 tusk
23–29 whales
23 bottle–nosed dolphin (bottle-nose dolphin)
24 common dolphin
25 sperm whale (cachalot)
26 blowhole (spout hole)
27 dorsal fin
28 flipper
29 tail flukes (tail)

80 Mammals III

1-11 **carnivores** (beasts of prey)
1 striped hyena, a hyena
2-8 **felines** (cats)
2 lion
3 mane (lion's mane)
4 paw
5 tiger
6 leopard
7 cheetah (hunting leopard)
8 lynx
9-11 **bears**
9 raccoon (racoon, *Am.* coon)
10 brown bear
11 polar bear (white bear)
12-16 **primates**
12-13 monkeys
12 rhesus monkey (rhesus, rhesus macaque)
13 baboon
14-16 **anthropoids** (anthropoid apes, great apes)
14 chimpanzee
15 orang-utan (orang-outan)
16 gorilla

1 Gigantocypris agassizi
2 Macropharynx longicaudatus
(pelican eel)
3 Pentacrinus (feather star), a sea
lily, an echinoderm
4 Thaumatolampas diadema, a
cuttlefish [luminescent]
5 Atolla, a deep-sea medusa, a
coelenterate
6 Melanocetes, a pediculate
[luminescent]
7 Lophocalyx philippensis, a glass
sponge
8 Mopsea, a sea fan [colony]
9 Hydrallmania, a hydroid polyp, a
coelenterate [colony]
10 Malacosteus indicus, a stomiatid
[luminescent]
11 Brisinga endecacnemos, a sand
star (brittle star), an echinoderm
[luminescent only when
stimulated]
12 Pasiphaea, a shrimp, a
crustacean
13 Echiostoma, a stomiatid, a fish
[luminescent]
14 Umbellula encrinus, a sea pen
(sea feather), a coelenterate
[colony, luminescent]
15 Polycheles, a crustacean
16 Lithodes, a crustacean, a crab
17 Archaster, a starfish (sea star), an
echinoderm
18 Oneirophanta, a sea cucumber,
an echinoderm
19 Palaeopneustes niasicus, a sea
urchin (sea hedgehog), an
echinoderm
20 Chitonactis, a sea anemone
(actinia), a coelenterate

82 General Botany

1 tree
2 bole (tree trunk, trunk, stem)
3 crown of tree (crown)
4 top of tree (treetop)
5 bough (limb, branch)
6 twig (branch)
7 bole (tree trunk) [cross section]
8 bark (rind)
9 phloem (bast sieve tissue, inner fibrous bark)
10 cambium (cambium ring)
11 medullary rays (vascular rays, pith rays)
12 sapwood (sap, alburnum)
13 heartwood (duramen)
14 pith
15 **plant**
16-18 root
16 primary root
17 secondary root
18 root hair
19-25 shoot (sprout)
19 leaf
20 stalk
21 side shoot (offshoot)
22 terminal bud
23 flower
24 flower bud
25 leaf axil with axillary bud
26 **leaf**
27 leaf stalk (petiole)
28 leaf blade (blade, lamina)
29 venation (veins, nervures, ribs)
30 midrib (nerve)
31-38 leaf shapes
31 linear
32 lanceolate
33 orbicular (orbiculate)
34 acerose (acerous, acerate, acicular, needle-shaped)
35 cordate
36 ovate
37 sagittate
38 reniform
39-42 compound leaves
39 digitate (digitated, palmate, quinquefoliolate)
40 pinnatifid
41 abruptly pinnate
42 odd-pinnate
43-50 leaf margin shapes
43 entire
44 serrate (serrulate, saw-toothed)
45 doubly toothed
46 crenate
47 dentate
48 sinuate
49 ciliate (ciliated)
50 cilium
51 **flower**
52 flower stalk (flower stem, scape)
53 receptacle (floral axis, thalamus, torus)
54 ovary
55 style
56 stigma
57 stamen
58 sepal
59 petal
60 ovary and stamen [section]
61 ovary wall
62 ovary cavity
63 ovule
64 embryo sac
65 pollen
66 pollen tube
67-77 inflorescences
67 spike (racemose spike)
68 raceme (simple raceme)
69 panicle
70 cyme
71 spadix (fleshy spike)
72 umbel (simple umbel)
73 capitulum
74 composite head (discoid flower head)
75 hollow flower head
76 bostryx (helicoid cyme)
77 cincinnus (scorpioid cyme, curled cyme)
78-82 roots
78 adventitious roots
79 tuber (tuberous root, swollen taproot)
80 adventitious roots (aerial roots)
81 root thorns
82 pneumatophores
83-85 blade of grass
83 leaf sheath
84 ligule (ligula)
85 leaf blade (lamina)
86 embryo (seed, germ)
87 cotyledon (seed leaf, seed lobe)
88 radicle
89 hypocotyl
90 plumule (leaf bud)
91-102 fruits
91-96 dehiscent fruits
91 follicle
92 legume (pod)
93 siliqua (pod)
94 schizocarp
95 pyxidium (circumscissile seed vessel)
96 poricidal capsule (porose capsule)
97-102 indehiscent fruits
97 berry
98 nut
99 drupe (stone fruit) (cherry)
100 aggregate fruit (compound fruit) (rose hip)
101 aggregate fruit (compound fruit) (raspberry)
102 pome (apple)

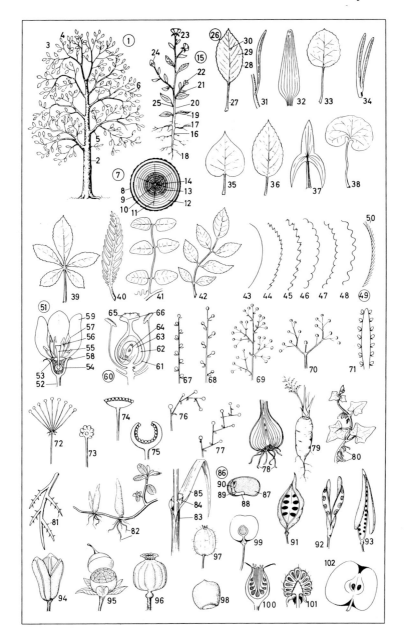

83 Deciduous Trees

84 Conifers

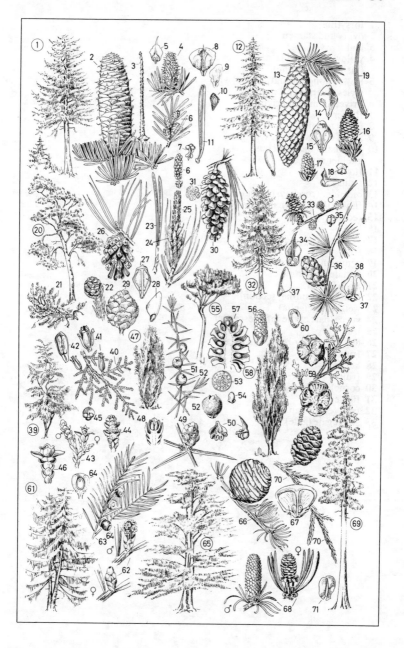

85 Ornamental Shrubs and Trees I

1 forsythia
2 ovary and stamen
3 leaf
4 yellow–flowered jasmine
   (jasmin, jessamine)
5 flower [longitudinal section] with
   styles, ovaries and stamens
6 privet (common privet)
7 flower
8 infructescence
9 mock orange (sweet syringa)
10 snowball (snowball bush,
   guelder rose)
11 flower
12 fruits
13 oleander (rosebay, rose laurel)
14 flower [longitudinal section]
15 red magnolia
16 leaf
17 japonica (japanese quince)
18 fruit
19 common box (box, box tree)
20 female flower
21 male flower
22 fruit [longitudinal section]
23 weigela (weigelia)
24 yucca [part of the inflorescence]
25 leaf
26 dog rose (briar rose, wild briar)
27 fruit
28 kerria
29 fruit
30 cornelian cherry
31 flower
32 fruit (cornelian cherry)
33 sweet gale (gale)

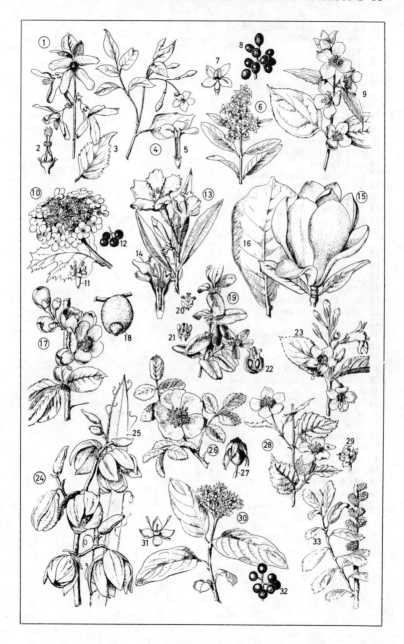

86 Ornamental Shrubs and Trees II

1 tulip tree (tulip poplar, saddle
  tree, whitewood)
2 carpels
3 stamen
4 fruit
5 hyssop
6 flower [front view]
7 flower
8 calyx with fruit
9 holly
10 androgynous (hermaphroditic,
  hermaphrodite) flower
11 male flower
12 fruit with stones exposed
13 honeysuckle (woodbine,
  woodbind)
14 flower buds
15 flower [cut open]
16 Virginia creeper (American ivy,
  woodbine)
17 open flower
18 infructescence
19 fruit [longitudinal section]
20 broom
21 flower with the petals removed
22 immature (unripe) legume (pod)
23 spiraea
24 flower [longitudinal section]
25 fruit
26 carpel
27 blackthorn (sloe)
28 leaves
29 fruits
30 single-pistilled hawthorn (thorn,
  may)
31 fruit
32 laburnum (golden chain, golden
  rain)
33 raceme
34 fruits
35 black elder (elder)
36 elder flowers (cymes)
37 elderberries

87 Meadow Flowers and Wayside Flowers (Wild Flowers) I

1 rotundifoliate (rotundifolious)
  saxifrage (rotundifoliate
  breakstone)
2 leaf
3 flower
4 fruit
5 anemone (windflower)
6 flower [longitudinal section]
7 fruit
8 buttercup (meadow buttercup,
  butterflower, goldcup, king cup,
  crowfoot)
9 basal leaf
10 fruit
11 lady's smock (ladysmock, cuckoo
  flower)
12 basal leaf
13 fruit
14 harebell (hairbell, bluebell)
15 basal leaf
16 flower [longitudinal section]
17 fruit
18 ground ivy (ale hoof)
19 flower [longitudinal section]
20 flower [front view]
21 stonecrop
22 speedwell
23 flower
24 fruit
25 seed
26 moneywort
27 dehisced fruit
28 seed
29 small scabious
30 basal leaf
31 flower of outer series
32 flower of inner series
33 involucral calyx with pappus
  bristles
34 ovary with pappus
35 fruit
36 lesser celandine
37 fruit
38 leaf axil with bulbil
39 annual meadow grass
40 flower
41 spikelet [side view]
42 spikelet [front view]
43 caryopsis (indehiscent fruit)
44 tuft of grass (clump of grass)
45 comfrey
46 flower [longitudinal section]
47 fruit

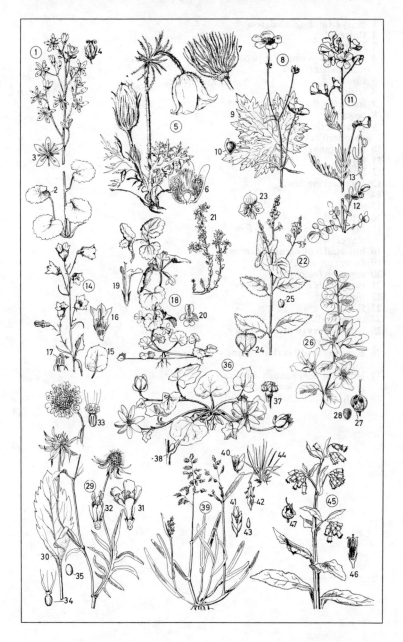

88 Meadow Flowers and Wayside Flowers (Wild Flowers) II

1 daisy (*Am.* English daisy)
2 flower
3 fruit
4 oxeye daisy (white oxeye daisy, marguerite)
5 flower
6 fruit
7 masterwort
8 cowslip
9 great mullein (Aaron's rod, shepherd's club)
10 bistort (snakeweed)
11 flower
12 knapweed
13 common mallow
14 fruit
15 yarrow
16 self-heal
17 bird's foot trefoil (bird's foot clover)
18 horsetail (equisetum) [a shoot]
19 flower (strobile)
20 campion (catchfly)
21 ragged robin (cuckoo flower)
22 birth-wort
23 flower
24 crane's bill
25 wild chicory (witloof, succory, wild endive)
26 common toadflax (butter-and-eggs)
27 lady's slipper (Venus's slipper, *Am.* moccasin flower)
28 orchis (wild orchid), an orchid

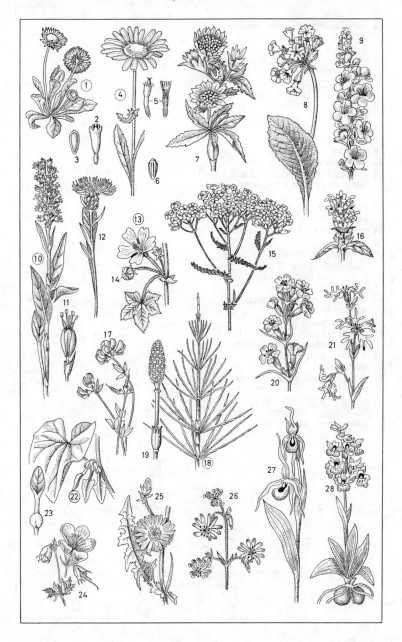

89 Plants of Forest, Marsh, and Heathland

1 wood anemone (anemone, windflower)
2 lily of the valley
3 cat's foot (milkwort); *sim.:* sandflower (everlasting)
4 turk's cap (turk's cap lily)
5 goatsbeard (goat's beard)
6 ramson
7 lungwort
8 corydalis
9 orpine (livelong)
10 daphne
11 touch-me-not
12 staghorn (stag horn moss, stag's horn, stag's horn moss, coral evergreen)
13 butterwort, an insectivorous plant
14 sundew; *sim.:* Venus's flytrap
15 bearberry
16 polypody (polypod), a fern; *sim.:* male fern, brake (bracken, eagle fern), royal fern (royal osmund, king's fern, ditch fern)
17 haircap moss (hair moss, golden maidenhair), a moss
18 cotton grass (cotton rush)
19 heather (heath, ling); *sim.:* bell heather (cross-leaved heather)
20 rock rose (sun rose)
21 marsh tea
22 sweet flag (sweet calamus, sweet sedge)
23 bilberry (whortleberry, huckleberry, blueberry); *sim.:* cowberry (red whortleberry), bog bilberry (bog whortleberry), crowberry (crakeberry)

90 Alpine Plants, Aquatic Plants (Water Plants), and Marsh Plants

1-13 alpine plants
1 alpine rose (alpine rhododendron)
2 flowering shoot
3 alpine soldanella (soldanella)
4 corolla opened out
5 seed vessel with the style
6 alpine wormwood
7 inflorescence
8 auricula
9 edelweiss
10 flower shapes
11 fruit with pappus tuft
12 part of flower head (of capitulum)
13 stemless alpine gentian
14-57 aquatic plants (water plants) and marsh plants
14 white water lily
15 leaf
16 flower
17 Queen Victoria water lily (Victoria regia water lily, royal water lily, Amazon water lily)
18 leaf
19 underside of the leaf
20 flower
21 reed mace bulrush (cattail, cat's tail, cattail flag, club rush)
22 male part of the spadix
23 male flower
24 female part
25 female flower
26 forget-me-not
27 flowering shoot
28 flower [section]
29 frog's bit
30 watercress
31 stalk with flowers and immature (unripe) fruits
32 flower
33 siliqua (pod) with seeds
34 two seeds
35 duckweed (duck's meat)
36 plant in flower
37 flower
38 fruit
39 flowering rush
40 flower umbel
41 leaves
42 fruit
43 green alga
44 water plantain

45 leaf
46 panicle
47 flower
48 honey wrack, a brown alga
49 thallus (plant body, frond)
50 holdfast
51 arrow head
52 leaf shapes
53 inflorescence with male flowers [above] and female flowers [below]
54 sea grass
55 inflorescence
56 Canadian waterweed (Canadian pondweed)
57 flower

91 Poisonous Plants

1 aconite (monkshood, wolfsbane, helmet flower)
2 foxglove (Digitalis)
3 meadow saffron (naked lady, naked boys)
4 hemlock (Conium)
5 black nightshade (common nightshade, petty morel)
6 henbane
7 deadly nightshade (belladonna, banewort, dwale), a solanaceous herb
8 thorn apple (stramonium, stramony, *Am.* jimson weed, jimpson weed, Jamestown weed, stinkweed)
9 cuckoo pint (lords–and–ladies, wild arum, wake–robin)
10-13 poisonous fungi (poisonous mushrooms, toadstools)
10 fly agaric (fly amanita, fly fungus), an agaric
11 amanita
12 Satan's mushroom
13 woolly milk cap

92 Medicinal Plants

1 camomile (chamomile, wild
  camomile)
2 arnica
3 peppermint
4 wormwood (absinth)
5 valerian (allheal)
6 fennel
7 lavender
8 coltsfoot
9 tansy
10 centaury
11 ribwort (ribwort plantain,
  ribgrass)
12 marshmallow
13 alder buckthorn (alder dogwood)
14 castor-oil plant (Palma Christi)
15 opium poppy
16 senna (cassia); *the dried leaflets:*
  senna leaves
17 cinchona (chinchona)
18 camphor tree (camphor laurel)
19 betel palm (areca, areca palm)
20 betel nut (areca nut)

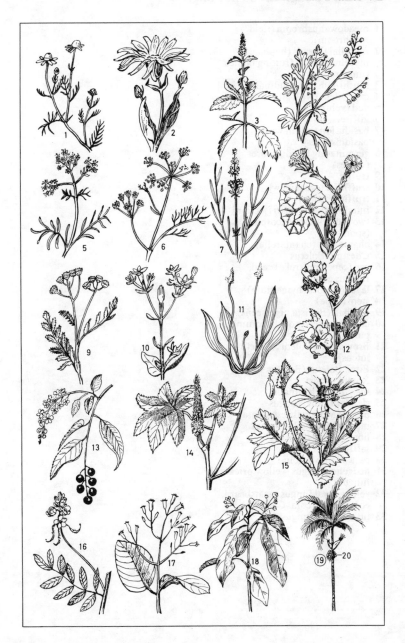

93 Edible Fungi (Esculent Fungi)

1 meadow mushroom (field mushroom)
2 mycelial threads (hyphae, mycelium) with fruiting bodies (mushrooms)
3 mushroom [longitudinal section]
4 cap (pileus) with gills
5 veil (velum)
6 gill [section]
7 basidia [on the gill with basidiospores]
8 germinating basidiospores (spores)
9 truffle
10 truffle [external view]
11 truffle [section]
12 interior showing asci [section]
13 two asci with the ascospores (spores)
14 chanterelle (chantarelle)
15 Chestnut Boletus
16 cep (cepe, squirrel's bread, Boletus edulis)
17 layer of tubes (hymenium)
18 stem (stipe)
19 puffball (Bovista nigrescens)
20 devil's tobacco pouch (common puffball)
21 Brown Ring Boletus (Boletus luteus)
22 Birch Boletus (Boletus scaber)
23 Russula vesca
24 scaled prickle fungus
25 slender funnel fungus
26 morel (Morchella esculenta)
27 morel (Morchella conica)
28 honey fungus
29 saffron milk cap
30 parasol mushroom
31 hedgehog fungus (yellow prickle fungus)
32 yellow coral fungus (goatsbeard, goat's beard, coral Clavaria)
33 little cluster fungus

94 Tropical Plants used as Stimulants, Spices, and Flavourings (*Am.* Flavorings)

1 coffee tree (coffee plant)
2 fruiting branch
3 flowering branch
4 flower
5 fruit with two beans [longitudinal section]
6 coffee bean; *when processed:* coffee
7 tea plant (tea tree)
8 flowering branch
9 tea leaf; *when processed:* tea
10 fruit
11 maté shrub (maté, yerba maté, Paraguay tea)
12 flowering branch with androgynous (hermaphroditic, hermaphrodite) flowers
13 male flower
14 androgynous (hermaphroditic, hermaphrodite) flower
15 fruit
16 cacao tree (cacao)
17 branch with flowers and fruits
18 flower [longitudinal section]
19 cacao beans (cocoa beans); *when processed:* cocoa, cocoa powder
20 seed [longitudinal section]
21 embryo
22 cinnamon tree (cinnamon)
23 flowering branch
24 fruit
25 cinnamon bark; *when crushed:* cinnamon
26 clove tree
27 flowering branch
28 flower bud; *when dried:* clove
29 flower
30 nutmeg tree
31 flowering branch
32 female flower [longitudinal section]
33 mature (ripe) fruit
34 nutmeg with mace, a seed with laciniate aril
35 seed [cross section]; *when dried:* nutmeg
36 pepper plant
37 fruiting branch
38 inflorescence
39 fruit [longitudinal section] with seed (peppercorn); *when ground:* pepper
40 Virginia tobacco plant

41 flowering shoot
42 flower
43 tobacco leaf; *when cured:* tobacco
44 mature (ripe) fruit capsule
45 seed
46 vanilla plant
47 flowering shoot
48 vanilla pod; *when cured:* stick of vanilla
49 pistachio tree
50 flowering branch with female flowers
51 drupe (pistachio, pistachio nut)
52 sugar cane
53 plant in bloom
54 panicle
55 flower

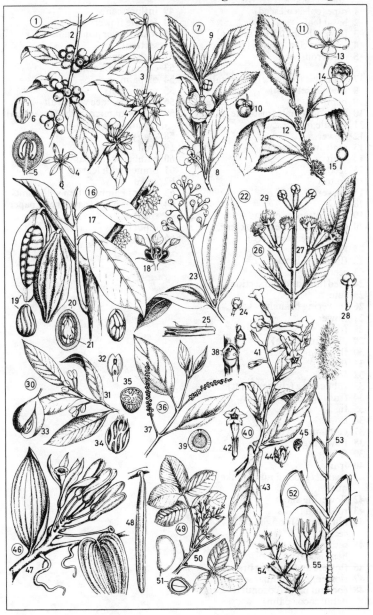

95 Plants used in Industry

1 rape (cole, coleseed)
2 basal leaf
3 flower [longitudinal section]
4 mature (ripe) siliqua (pod)
5 oleiferous seed
6 flax
7 peduncle (pedicel, flower stalk)
8 seed vessel (boll)
9 hemp
10 fruiting female (pistillate) plant
11 female inflorescence
12 flower
13 male inflorescence
14 fruit
15 seed
16 cotton
17 flower
18 fruit
19 lint [cotton wool]
20 silk-cotton tree (kapok tree, capoc tree, ceiba tree)
21 fruit
22 flowering branch
23 seed
24 seed [longitudinal section]
25 jute
26 flowering branch
27 flower
28 fruit
29 olive tree (olive)
30 flowering branch
31 flower
32 fruit
33 rubber tree (rubber plant)
34 fruiting branch
35 fig
36 flower
37 gutta-percha tree
38 flowering branch
39 flower
40 fruit
41 peanut (ground nut, monkey nut)
42 flowering shoot
43 root with fruits
44 nut (kernel) [longitudinal section]
45 sesame plant (simsim, benniseed)
46 flowers and fruiting branch
47 flower [longitudinal section]
48 coconut palm (coconut tree, coco palm, cocoa palm)

49 inflorescence
50 female flower
51 male flower [longitudinal section]
52 fruit [longitudinal section]
53 coconut (cokernut)
54 oil palm
55 male spadix
56 infructescence with fruit
57 seed with micropyles (foramina) (foraminate seed)
58 sago palm
59 fruit
60 bamboo stem (bamboo culm)
61 branch with leaves
62 spike
63 part of bamboo stem with joints
64 papyrus plant (paper reed, paper rush)
65 umbel
66 spike

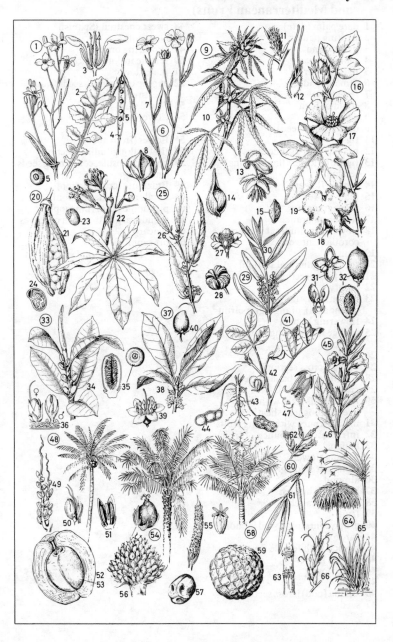

96 Southern Fruits (Tropical, Subtropical, and Mediterranean Fruits)

1 date palm (date)
2 fruiting palm
3 palm frond
4 male spadix
5 male flower
6 female spadix
7 female flower
8 stand of fruit
9 date
10 date kernel (seed)
11 fig
12 branch with pseudocarps
13 fig with flowers [longitudinal section]
14 female flower
15 male flower
16 pomegranate
17 flowering branch
18 flower [longitudinal section, corolla removed]
19 fruit
20 seed [longitudinal section]
21 seed [cross section]
22 embryo
23 lemon; *sim.*: tangerine (mandarin), orange, grapefruit
24 flowering branch
25 orange flower [longitudinal section]
26 fruit
27 orange [cross section]
28 banana plant (banana tree)
29 crown
30 herbaceous stalk with overlapping leaf sheaths
31 inflorescence with young fruits
32 infructescence (bunch of fruit)
33 banana
34 banana flower
35 banana leaf [diagram]
36 almond
37 flowering branch
38 fruiting branch
39 fruit
40 drupe containing seed [almond]
41 carob
42 branch with female flowers
43 female flower
44 male flower
45 fruit
46 siliqua (pod) [cross section]
47 seed

48 sweet chestnut (Spanish chestnut)
49 flowering branch
50 female inflorescence
51 male flower
52 cupule containing seeds (nuts, chestnuts)
53 Brazil nut
54 flowering branch
55 leaf
56 flower [from above]
57 flower [longitudinal section]
58 opened capsule, containing seeds (nuts)
59 Brazil nut [cross section]
60 nut [longitudinal section]
61 pineapple plant (pineapple)
62 pseudocarp with crown of leaves
63 syncarp
64 pineapple flower
65 flower [longitudinal section]

Ordering of Entries

In the index the entries are ordered as follows:
1. Entries consisting of single words, e.g.: 'hair'.
2. Entries consisting of noun + adjective. Within this category the adjectives are entered alphabetically, e.g. 'hair, bobbed' is followed by 'hair, closely-cropped'.

   Where adjective and noun are regarded as elements of a single lexical item, they are not inverted, e.g.: 'blue spruce', not 'spruce, blue'.
3. Entries consisting of other phrases, e.g. 'hair curler', 'ham on the bone', are alphabetized as headwords.

Where a whole phrase makes the meaning or use of a headword highly specific, the whole phrase is entered alphabetically. For example 'ham on the bone' follows 'hammock'.

Index

Agr.	Agriculture/Agricultural	*Hydr. Eng.*	Hydraulic Engineering
Alp. Plants	Alpine Plants	*Impl.*	Implements
Art. Studio	Artist's Studio	*Inf. Tech.*	Information Technology
Bldg.	Building	*Intern. Combust. Eng.*	Internal Combustion Engine
Carp.	Carpenter	*Moon L.*	Moon Landing
Cement Wks.	Cement Works	*Music Not.*	Musical Notation
Cost.	Costumes	*Overh. Irrign.*	Overhead Irrigation
Cyc.	Cycle	*Platem.*	Platemaking
Decid.	Deciduous	*Plant. Propagn.*	Propagation of Plants
D.I.Y.	Do-it-yourself	*Rm.*	Room
Dom. Anim.	Domestic Animals	*Sp.*	Sports
Equest.	Equestrian Sport	*Text.*	Textile[s]
Gdn.	Garden	*Veg.*	Vegetable[s]

A

Aaron's rod **88** 9
abdomen *Bees* **50** 10-19
abdomen *Forest Pests* **55** 9
abdomen *Man* **16** 35-37, 36
abdomen, lower ~ **16** 37
abdomen, upper ~ **16** 35
abductor hallucis **18** 49
abductor of the hallux **18** 49
aberdevine **73** 8
abrasion platform **13** 31
abscissa **63** 9
absinth **92** 4
absorber attachment **27** 44
acceleration lane **15** 16
accelerator lock **58** 17
access flap **6** 21, 25
accipiters **74** 10-13
acerate **82** 34
acerose **82** 34
acerous **82** 34
achene **31** 23
Achilles' tendon **18** 48
acicular **82** 34
acid container **66** 62
Ackermann steering system **58** 31, 37
aconite **91** 1
acorn **83** 4
actinia **81** 20
Actinophrys **69** 7
activated blade attachment **57** 33
Adam's apple **19** 13
adders **76** 40-41
adding **60** 23
addition **60** 23
adjustment, circular ~ **14** 62
adjustment knob **11** 41
administration area **5** 17
adult insect **70** 10
advertising calendar **22** 10
aerator **29** 15
Afghan **43** 23
Afghan hound **43** 23
Africa **14** 14
African marigold **33** 20

agaric **91** 10
agitator *Agr. Mach.* **37** 70
agricultural implements **39**
agricultural machinery **37**; **38**
agricultural worker **36** 5
agriculture **36**
Agulhas Current **14** 37
air-conditioning **26** 20
air currents **9** 25-29
air line **48** 28
air masses, homogeneous ~ **8** 1-4
air regulator *Chem.* **66** 3, 8
air space **47** 61
airstream, cold ~ **9** 29
airstream, warm ~ **9** 28
air survey camera **14** 63
aisle *Forestry* **57** 1
aisle *Map* **15** 112
albumen **47** 62
alburnum *Bot.* **82** 12
Alcor **3** 29
Aldebaran **3** 25
alder **83** 30
alder buckthorn **92** 13
alder dogwood **92** 13
alder-swamp peat **13** 18
ale hoof **87** 18
alga, brown ~ **90** 48
alga, green ~ **90** 43
algebra **61** 4-5
alighting board **50** 49
allheal **92** 5
all-purpose trailer **35** 40
almond *South. Fruits* **96** 36
alpha particle **1** 30-31; **2** 27
alpha ray **1** 30-31
alpine rhododendron **90** 1
alpine rose **90** 1
alpine soldanella **90** 3
alpine strawberry **31** 16
alpine wormwood **90** 6
Alsatian **43** 25
alsike **42** 3
alsike clover **42** 3
Altair **3** 9
altitude **62** 27
altitude scale **7** 35

altocumulus **8** 15
altocumulus castellanus **8** 16
altocumulus floccus **8** 16
altostratus **8** 8
altostratus praecipitans **8** 9
amanita **91** 11
Amazon water lily **90** 17
America **14** 12-13
American blight **53** 32
American ivy **86** 16
amoeba **69** 1
Amphibia **76** 20-26
amphibians **76** 20-26
amplitude adjustment **10** 11
anaesthesia and breathing apparatus **26** 1
anaesthesia and respiratory apparatus **26** 24
anaesthetic, local ~ **24** 53
analyser **23** 53
analysis, automatic ~ **25** 48
analytical balance **65** 25
Andromeda **3** 24
anemometer **10** 28
anemone **87** 5; **89** 1
aneroid barometer **10** 4
aneroid box **10** 6
aneroid capsule **10** 6
angiographic examination table **27** 26
angiography room **27** 12
angle *Maths.* **62** 1-23; **62** 8-13, 55
angle, acute ~ **62** 10
angle, adjacent ~ **62** 14
angle, alternate ~ **62** 10
angle, circumferential ~ **62** 56
angle, exterior ~ **62** 26
angle, interior ~ **62** 26
angle, obtuse ~ **62** 11
angle, straight ~ **62** 13, 9-15
angle of dip **12** 3
angle of rotation **67** 33
angle of the mouth **16** 14; **19** 19
angle symbol **61** 23
Angora cat **46** 17
Angoumois grain moth **54** 29

181

Angoumois grain moth caterpillar

banana leaf **96** 35
banana plant **96** 28
banana tree **96** 28
bandage *First Aid* **21** 9
bandages, emergency ~ **21** 1-13
banewort **91** 7
bank *Phys. Geog.* **13** 4
bantam **47** 56
barb *Bees* **50** 10
barbel **76** 13
barchan **13** 40
barchane **13** 40
bar *Horse* **44** 41
bark *Bot.* **82** 8
bark beetle **55** 22
bark brush **29** 23
barkhan **13** 40
barking **58** 23
barking iron **58** 8
bark scraper **29** 14
bark spud **58** 8
bark stripping **58** 23
barley **41** 1, 26
barn owl **74** 17
barn swallow **73** 20
barograph **10** 4
bars **48** 5
bar, sliding ~ **48** 21
barysphere **11** 5
basal pinacoid **67** 20
base *Maths.* **61** 1, 6; **62** 27; **63** 35, 39
basidia **93** 7
basidiospore **93** 8
basilisk *Fish etc.* **76** 30
basin *Dent.* **24** 12
basin *Doc.* **23** 25
basket, wire ~ **28** 50; **39** 25
batch of eggs **53** 2, 30
batholite **11** 29
bath sponge *Invertebr.* **69** 13
batrachians **76** 23-26
battery *Agr. Mach.* **38** 53
battery *Poultry Farm* **47** 19
battery cage **47** 20
battery feeding **47** 23
battery system **47** 18
battery tester **25** 52
baulk *Agr.* **36** 3
bay *Phys. Geog.* **13** 7
beach **13** 35-44
beach, raised ~ **11** 54
beach grass **15** 7
beach marten **79** 14
beacon **15** 10, 49
beaker **66** 20
beak, hooked ~ **74** 6
beam *Agr. Mach.* **38** 9, 71
beam *Chem.* **65** 30
beam, central ~ **27** 3
beam entry point **1** 64
bean **30** 8, 11
bean, bush ~ **30** 8
bean, climbing ~ **30** 8
bean flower **30** 9
bean plant **30** 8
beanstalk **30** 10
bearberry **89** 15
beard *Arable Crops* **41** 12
beard *Dom. Anim.* **46** 15

bearded couch grass **34** 30
bearing, hydrostatic ~ **5** 10
bears **80** 9-11
beasts of prey **79** 11-22; **80** 1-11
beater, revolving ~ **37** 13
beaver *Mammals* **78** 14
bed *Hosp.* **25** 10
bed *Phys. Geog.* **13** 49
bed, rear ~ **58** 49
bed bug **54** 39
Bedlington terrier **43** 18
bed monitor **25** 19
bedrock **13** 70
bee **50** 1-25
bee, male ~ **50** 5
beech gall **55** 37
beech nut **83** 37
beech tree **83** 33
bee eater **72** 2
beehive **50** 45-50
bee house **50** 56
beekeeper **50** 57
beekeeping **50**
beeman **50** 57
bees **50**
bee shed **50** 51
bee smoker **50** 59
bee sting ointment **50** 68
beeswax **50** 67
beet **41** 44, 45
beet carrion beetle **53** 45
beet cleaner **37** 89
beet elevator **37** 94
beet elevator belt **37** 95
beet harvester **37** 85-96
beet hopper **37** 96
beetle **55** 26, 42
beetles **70** 24-39
beet leaf **41** 47
beet top **41** 46
bee veil **50** 58
belladonna **91** 7
Bellatrix **3** 13
belly-band **44** 36
bench torch **66** 9
Benguela Current **14** 43
benniseed **95** 45
berry **31** 9, 11; **82** 97
beta particle **1** 32
beta ray **1** 32
Betelgeuse **3** 13
betel nut **92** 20
betel palm **92** 19
biceps brachii **18** 37
biceps femoris **18** 61
Big Dipper **3** 29
bilberry **89** 23
bile duct, common ~ **20** 37-38
bill *Birds* **71** 17
billhook **29** 9; **58** 11
bindweed **34** 26
biopsy forceps **23** 17
biprism, ditrigonal ~ **67** 22
biprism, hexagonal ~ **67** 22
bipyramid, tetragonal ~ **67** 18
Birch Boletus **93** 22
birch tree **83** 9
bird, flightless ~ **71** 4
bird, gallinaceous ~ **71** 22
bird, migratory ~ **72** 7

bird, non-migratory ~ **72** 4
bird, resident ~ **72** 4
bird cherry **32** 5
bird-foot **42** 11
birds **71**; **73**; **74**; **75**
birds, corvine ~ **73** 1-3
birds, endemic ~ **72**
birds, exotic ~ **75**
birds, flightless ~ **71** 1-3
birds, indigenous ~ **72**
birds, long-winged ~ **71** 11-14
birds, web-footed ~ **71** 5-10
bird's foot **42** 11
bird's foot clover **88** 17
bird's foot trefoil **42** 11; **88** 17
birdsmouth **57** 28
birds of prey **74**
birds of prey, diurnal ~ **74** 1-13
birds of prey, nocturnal ~ **74** 14-19
birth-wort **88** 22
bisector **62** 28, 30
bison **79** 9
bistort **88** 10
bitch **46** 16
biting housefly **54** 4
black **59** 13
black arches moth **55** 17
black-backed jackal **79** 11
black beetle **54** 17
blackberry **31** 29
blackbird **73** 13
black buck **79** 5
black elder **86** 35
black-headed gull **71** 14
black nightshade **91** 5
black rhino **78** 25
black salsify **30** 35
blackthorn **86** 27
bladder **20** 33, 78
blade *Arable Crops* **41** 20
blade *Bot.* **82** 28
blade *Gdn. Tools* **29** 36
blade, flexible ~ **58** 20
blade, front ~ **58** 35
blade, lower ~ **23** 14
blade, rear ~ **58** 40
blade of grass **82** 83-85
blanket **44** 44
blastodisc **47** 65
bleeding heart **33** 5
blinder **44** 26
blind *Hosp.* **25** 9
blind spot **19** 50
blindworm **76** 37
blinker **44** 26
blob marker **56** 9
blob marking **56** 6
block mountain **12** 4-11
blood, arterial ~ **18** 12
blocd, venous ~ **18** 11
blood circulation **18** 1-21
blood flow **21** 14-17
blood pressure **23** 32; **25** 1
blood sedimentation **23** 42
blood smear **23** 50
blood vessel **19** 33
blossom **32** 9; **42** 14; **53** 11
blowfly **70** 18
blowhole **79** 26

C

chair, steel ~ **40** 2
chalaza **47** 63
Chamaeleontidae **76** 33
chamber *Atom* **1** 66
chamber *Forest Pests* **55** 36
chameleon **76** 33
chamois **79** 3
chamomile **34** 8; **92** 1
change gears **10** 14
channel, distributary ~ **13** 2
channel *Overh. Irrign.* **40** 13
chantarelle **93** 14
chanterelle **93** 14
chapel *Map* **15** 61, 107
chaps **43** 26
characteristic **61** 6
chard **30** 28
charger **25** 51
Charioteer **3** 27
Charles's Wain **3** 29
charlock **34** 18
chart **22** 32; **49** 8
chart, illustrated ~ **22** 16
chassis *Overh. Irrign.* **40** 14
cheekbone **16** 8; **17** 37
cheek *Man* **16** 9
cheek piece **44** 8
cheek strap **44** 8
cheesefly **54** 15
cheese machine **49** 47
cheetah **80** 7
chelicer **70** 41
cheliped **70** 41
chemistry laboratory **65**; **66**
cherry blossom **32** 3
cherry *Bot.* **82** 99
cherry *Drupes & Nuts* **32** 5, 6-8
cherry flower **32** 3
cherry fruit **32** 6-8
cherry fruit **32** 2
cherry leaf **32** 2
cherry stone **32** 7
cherry tree **32** 1, 11-18
chest grip **21** 37
chest *Man* **16** 28-30; **17** 8-11
Chestnut Boletus **93** 15
chestnut *Decid. Trees* **83** 60
chestnut *Horse* **45** 27
chestnut tree **83** 58
chick **47** 2
chicken **35** 36; **46** 19-26
chicken run **47** 11
chick-pea **42** 19
chick unit **47** 1
chicory **30** 40
chimney *Map* **15** 38
chimney swallow **73** 20
chimpanzee **80** 14
chin **16** 15
chinch **54** 39
chinchona **92** 17
chiropter **78** 9
chiropteran **78** 9
Chitonactis **81** 20
chive **30** 22
chlorine ion **1** 10
cholecystography **27** 4
chopper drum **37** 34
chord *Maths.* **62** 51
chow **43** 21

chrysalis **50** 30, 32; **53** 4, 25, 43; **54** 3, 21, 24; **55** 13, 21, 32; **70** 20; **77** 11
chrysanthemum **34** 7
church **15** 53, 61, 107
church landmark **15** 64
church owl **74** 11
cigarette beetle **54** 25
ciliate **82** 49
ciliate infusorian **69** 9
cilium *Bot.* **82** 50
cilium *Invertebr.* **69** 10
cilium *Man* **19** 41
cinchona **92** 17
cincinnus **82** 77
cinnamon **94** 25
cinnamon bark **94** 25
cinnamon tree **94** 22
circle *Maths.* **62** 42
circle, circumscribed ~ **62** 29
circle, divided ~ *Crystals* **67** 32
circle, graduated ~ *Crystals* **67** 32
circle, inscribed ~ **62** 31
circles, concentric ~ **62** 58
circles, polar ~ **14** 11
circular saw attachment **57** 33
circulation, atmospheric ~ **9** 46-52
circulatory system **18** 1-21
circumcircle **62** 29
circumference *Maths.* **62** 44
cirrocumulus **8** 14
cirrostratus **8** 7
cirrus **8** 6
city **15** 51
Claisen flask **66** 50
clamp *Chem.* **66** 33
clamp, horizontal ~ **14** 57
clamping device *Atom* **2** 43
clamp *Overh. Irrign.* **40** 30
clamp, vertical ~ **14** 55
classes, social ~ of bees **50** 1, 4, 5
clavicle **17** 6
claw, double ~ **50** 8
claw **74** 7
clay pit *Map* **15** 88
clear-felling system **57** 4-14
clearing *Forestry* **57** 13
clearing *Map* **15** 2
cleaving hammer **58** 5
cleft, anal ~ **16** 41
click beetle **53** 37, 38
cliff **13** 28
cliff face **13** 28
cliffline **13** 25-31
cliffs **13** 25-31
climate, artificially maintained ~ **68** 21
climate, boreal ~ **9** 56
climate, equatorial ~ **9** 53
climates **9** 53-58
climates, polar ~ **9** 57-58
climatic map **9** 40-58
climatology **9**
climber *Veg.* **30** 8
clinoprinacoid **67** 24
clip *Atom* **2** 18
clitellum **69** 26
clitoris **20** 88
clockwork drive **10** 14

clod **36** 7
clothes louse **54** 41
clothes moth **54** 13
clothing, protective ~ **57** 26
cloth, sterile ~ **26** 38
cloud chamber photograph **2** 26
cloud chamber track **2** 27
cloud cover **9** 20-24
clouds **8** 1-19, 1-4, 5-12, 13-17
clouds, luminous ~ **7** 22
clouds, noctilucent ~ **7** 22
clove **94** 28
clove carnation **33** 7
clove pink **33** 7
clover broadcaster **39** 26
clover, four-leaf ~ **42** 5
clove tree **94** 26
club rush **90** 21
clump of grass **87** 44
cluster of eggs **53** 2, 30
cluster of grapes **51** 5
cluster of stars **3** 26
clutch, fluid ~ **38** 37
clutch, main ~ **38** 39
coastal lake **13** 44
cob **32** 49
cobalt bomb **2** 28
cobnut **32** 49
coccinellid **70** 37
coccyx **17** 5; **20** 60
cochlea **17** 63
cockchafer **55** 1
cockchafer grub **55** 12
cock *Dom. Anim.* **46** 21
cocker spaniel **43** 38
cock *Farm Bldgs.* **35** 37
cock pigeon **46** 33
cockroach **54** 17
cockscomb **46** 22
cock's foot **42** 25
cock's head **42** 10
cock's tread **47** 65
cocoa bean **94** 19
cocoa palm **95** 48
cocoa powder **94** 19
cocoa *Trop. Plants* **94** 19
coconut **95** 53
coconut palm **95** 48
coconut tree **95** 48
cocoon *Articulates* **70** 51
cocoon *Forest Pests* **55** 21
coco palm **95** 48
codling moth **31** 62
codlin moth **31** 62
coefficient **61** 4
coelenterate **69** 14; **81** 5, 9, 14, 20
coffee bean **94** 6
coffee plant **94** 1
coffee tree **94** 1
coffee *Trop. Plants* **94** 6
cokernut **95** 53
col **12** 47
cold house **28** 33
cold light source **23** 8
cole **95** 1
Coleoptera **70** 24-39
coleseed **95** 1
collarbone **17** 6
collar *Dog* **43** 13
collar, Dutch ~ **44** 28

earth core **11** 5
earth moth **53** 42
earth, prepared ~ **28** 15
earthquake **11** 32-38
earthquake, submarine ~ **11** 53
earthquake focus **11** 32
earthworm **69** 24
ear tuft **74** 16
earwig **54** 11
East Australian Current **14** 38
easterlies **9** 48, 49
east point **4** 14
ECG **23** 28
ECG amplitude **25** 49
ECG analyser **25** 45
ECG analysis **25** 50
ECG impulse **25** 46
ECG lead **25** 43
ECG machine, portable ~ **23** 46
ECG monitor **25** 2, 21, 28, 47
ECG recorder **25** 41
ECG recording unit **25** 27
ECG rhythm **25** 48
echinoderm **81** 3, 11, 17, 18, 19
echinoderms **69** 38-39
Echiostoma **81** 13
eclipse **4** 33
eclipse, lunar ~ **4** 29-35, 34-35
eclipse, solar ~ **4** 29-35, 32, 39, 41
ecliptic **3** 2; **4** 22
edelweiss **90** 9
edge *Forestry* **58** 2
edge *Maths.* **63** 32
edging, hoop ~ **28** 38
eel **76** 17
egg *Articulates* **70** 49
egg *Bees* **50** 26, 27
egg *Forest Pests* **55** 19
egg *Gdn. Pests* **53** 15, 55
egg *Man* **20** 84
egg *Poultry Farm* **47** 58
egg box **47** 42, 45
egg collection **47** 22, 34
egg collection system **47** 34
egg gallery **55** 23
egg integument **47** 59
egg-packing machine, fully automatic ~ **47** 46
egg production **47** 34-53
eggshell **47** 59
egg weigher **47** 43
E-layer **7** 27
elbow *Horse* **45** 20
elbow *Man* **16** 45
elbow *Overh. Irrign.* **40** 6
elder **86** 35
elderberry **86** 37
elder flower **86** 36
electricity transmission line **15** 113
electrocardiogram monitor **25** 2, 21, 28
electrocardiograph **23** 28; **25** 41
electrode, central ~ **2** 3
electrode exit point **25** 34
electrode *Hosp.* **25** 26, 35, 38
electrode lead **25** 25
electrode, platinum-iridium ~ **24** 44

electrode, strap-on ~ **23** 30
electron **1** 3, 17, 27, 32
electron, free ~ **1** 25
electron shell **1** 6, 8
electron spin **1** 4
electrotome **22** 38
element, fissionable ~ **1** 49
element of set **64** 2
elephant **78** 20
elephant enclosure **68** 9
elephant house **68** 10
elevating drum, rotary ~ **37** 74
elevator, chain and slat ~ **37** 7
elevator, open-web ~ **37** 69
elk **79** 1, 2
ellipse **63** 22
ellipsoid of revolution **63** 42
elm tree **83** 49
elytron **55** 10; **70** 36
embankment *Map* **15** 104
embryo *Arable Crops* **41** 16
embryo *Bot.* **82** 86
embryo *South. Fruits* **96** 22
embryo *Trop. Plants* **94** 21
embryo plant **41** 14
embryo sac **82** 64
emÊ **71** 1
enamel **19** 30
enclosing wall **68** 4
enclosure, outdoor ~ **68** 1
endive **30** 39
end moraine **12** 55
energy **1** 55
energy level **1** 15, 27
energy system **6** 6, 8
engine *Moon L.* **6** 30
English daisy **88** 1
English ryegrass **42** 26
English setter **43** 41
entire **82** 43
entrance **50** 48
entry/exit hatch **6** 38
entry hatch **6** 10
ephemerid **70** 6
epicalyx **31** 22
epicenter **11** 33
epicentre **11** 33
epididymis **20** 73
epiglottis **17** 51
equals sign **60** 23
equation, conditional ~ **61** 9
equation, identical ~ **61** 5
equation, simple ~ **61** 4
equator **14** 1
equator, celestial ~ **3** 3
Equatorial Countercurrent **14** 33
equinoxes **3** 6-7
equisetum **88** 18
equitation **44** 1-6
erasion **26** 52
Ergates faber **70** 38
ergometer, bicycle ~ **23** 26
ergometry **23** 26-31
ergot **41** 4
Eridamus **3** 12
Erlenmeyer flask **66** 39
ermine moth **53** 5
erne **74** 5

eruption **7** 21
escarpment **13** 57
esophagus **17** 49
ethmoid **17** 39
Europe **14** 15
European silver fir **84** 1
European Southern Observatory **5** 1-16
European toad **76** 23
Euscorpius flavicandus **70** 40
evacuating pump, centrifugal ~ **40** 11, 23
evaporating basin **66** 29
evaporating dish **66** 29
everlasting **89** 3
evolution **61** 2
ewe **46** 13; **48** 10
examination couch **22** 43; **23** 4
examination table **27** 1, 26
excited state **1** 19
exclusion principle **1** 7
excretory vacuole **69** 5
exhaust *Agr. Mach.* **37** 38
exosphere **7** 31
expansion line **1** 61
explosion, atomic ~ **7** 11
exponent **61** 1
extensor carpi radialis longus **18** 56
extensor, common ~ **18** 57, 63
extensor, radial ~ **18** 56
extensor communis digitorum **18** 57, 63
extracting a root **61** 2
extraction forceps **24** 47
extremity, fimbriated ~ **20** 82
eyeball **19** 45
eye-bright **34** 27
eyebrow *Man* **19** 38
eye, compound ~ *Articulates* **70** 7
eye, compound ~ *Bees* **50** 20-24
eye *Dom. Anim.* **46** 32
eyeground **22** 32
eye *Horse* **45** 4
eyelash **19** 41
eyelid, lower ~ **19** 40
eyelid, upper ~ **19** 39
eye *Man* **16** 7; **19** 38-51
eye muscles **19** 44
eyepiece, binocular ~ **23** 6
eye, simple ~ **50** 2
eyespot **70** 54
eye, stalked ~ **69** 30

F

face *Horse* **45** 5
face *Man* **16** 4-17
facet **50** 20
facing **24** 32
factor **60** 25
fahlerz **67** 1
fahl ore **67** 1
fair-weather cumulus **8** 1
falcons **74** 1-4
falling wedge **58** 4
fallow **36** 1
falls **11** 45
false acacia **83** 70

flower *Decid. Trees* **83** 17, 26, 35, 40, 52, 55, 62
flower *Drupes & Nuts* **32** 9
flower *Flowers etc.* **87** 3, 6, 16, 19, 20, 23, 40, 46; **88** 2, 5, 11, 19, 23
flower *Fodder Plants* **42** 7, 14
flower, female ~ *Alp. Plants etc.* **90** 25; **90** 53
flower, female ~ *Conifers* **84** 43
flower, female ~ *Decid. Trees* **83** 6, 13
flower, female *Drupes & Nuts* **32** 38
flower, female ~ *Industr. Plants* **95** 50
flower, female ~ *Shrubs etc.* **85** 20
flower, female ~ *South. Fruits* **96** 7, 14, 42, 43
flower, female ~ *Trop. Plants* **94** 32, 50
flower, forced ~ **28** 24
flower, fumariaceous ~ **33** 5
flower *Gdn. Pests* **53** 11
flower head *Alp. Plants etc.* **90** 12
flower head *Weeds* **34** 14
flower head, discoid ~ **82** 74
flower head, hollow ~ **82** 75
flower, hermaphroditic ~ *Shrubs etc.* **86** 10
flower, hermaphroditic ~ *Trop. Plants* **94** 12, 14
flower *Industr. Plants* **95** 12, 17, 27, 31, 36, 39, 46, 47
flowering branch *Decid. Trees* **83** 2, 10, 16, 34, 39, 51, 54, 66, 71
flowering branch *Industr. Plants* **95** 22, 26, 30, 38
flowering branch *South. Fruits* **96** 17, 24, 37, 49, 54
flowering rush **90** 39
flowering shoot *Alp. Plants etc.* **90** 2, 27
flowering shoot *Industr. Plants* **95** 42
flowering shoot *Trop. Plants* **94** 41, 47
flower, male ~ *Alp. Plants etc.* **90** 23, 53
flower, male ~ *Conifers* **84** 43
flower, male ~ *Decid. Trees* **83** 14
flower, male ~ *Drupes & Nuts* **32** 39
flower, male ~ *Industr. Plants* **95** 51
flower, male ~ *Shrubs etc.* **85** 21; **86** 11
flower, male ~ *South. Fruits* **96** 5, 15, 44, 51
flower, male ~ *Trop. Plants* **94** 13
flower, open ~ **86** 17
flower shoot **32** 28
flower shoot, male ~ **84** 6, 62, 68
flower *Shrubs etc.* **85** 5, 7, 11, 14, 31; **86** 6, 7, 15, 21, 24
flower *Soft Fruit* **31** 4
flower *South. Fruits* **96** 13, 18, 56, 57, 65

flower stalk *Bot.* **82** 52
flower stalk *Industr. Plants* **95** 7
flower stem **82** 52
flowers, wild ~ **87**; **88**
flower *Trop. Plants* **94** 4, 17, 18, 29, 42, 55
flower *Weeds* **34** 10, 19, 22
flower, withered ~ **31** 55
flower umbel **90** 40
flowmeter *Dairy.* **49** 4
flowmeter *Hosp.* **26** 3
fluorite **67** 16
fluoroscope, mobile ~ **26** 14
fluorspar **67** 16
fluothane container **26** 26
fly agaric **91** 10
fly amanita **91** 10
fly *Articulates* **70** 18
fly fungus **91** 10
fly swat **56** 32
foal **46** 2
foam canister **56** 6
foam feed pipe **56** 10
focus **63** 25, 27
focusing device **5** 11
focus, seismic ~ **11** 32
fodder plants **42** 1-28
fodder silo **35** 11, 43
fog **9** 31
fog, high ~ **8** 4
fold, asymmetrical ~ **12** 13
fold, gluteal ~ **16** 42
folding **12** 4-20
fold mountains **12** 12-20
fold, nasolabial ~ **16** 11
fold, normal ~ **12** 12
fold, reclined ~ **12** 15
fold, recumbent ~ **12** 15
fold, symmetrical ~ **12** 12
fold unit **47** 1
follicle *Bot.* **82** 91
follicle *Man* **20** 84
food pests **54** 15-30
food vacuole **69** 6
footbridge **15** 78
foot ferry **15** 60
foot lever **56** 34
foot *Man* **16** 54; **17** 26-29; **19** 52-63
foot muscle **18** 49
foot, palmate ~ **46** 36; **71** 7
foot passenger ferry **15** 60
footpath **15** 43
footpath under railway **15** 44
foot pedal *Pest Contr.* **56** 34
foot, prehensile ~ **76** 34
foot, webbed ~ **46** 36; **71** 6, 7
foot switch *Hosp.* **27** 21
foot treadle **56** 34
forage harvester, self-propelled ~ **37** 34-39
forage plants **42** 1-28
foramen **95** 57
forceps **22** 52
forceps, obstetrical ~ **26** 53
forcing bed **28** 16
forcing house **28** 4
forearm *Horse* **45** 21
forearm *Man* **16** 46
forecarriage **38** 14-19

forefinger **19** 65
forefoot **45** 22-26
forehand **45** 18-27
forehead *Horse* **45** 3
forehead *Man* **16** 4-5
foreleg **43** 5
forelock **45** 2
forepaw **43** 6
foreskin **20** 70
forest **57** 1-34
forest labourer **57** 18
forest pests **55**
forestry **57**; **58**
forestry office **15** 3
forest track **57** 3
forewing **70** 36
forget-me-not **90** 26
fork *Agr. Impl.* **39** 3, 7, 22
fork *Horse* **44** 29
forsythia **85** 1
fortress **15** 74
fossette **16** 16
foundation *Bees* **50** 43
foundation pile **5** 28
fowl, domestic ~ **46** 19-36
fowl run **47** 11
foxglove **91** 2
fox terrier, wire-haired ~ **43** 15
foyer **5** 25
fraction **60** 10, 19
fraction, complex ~ **60** 17
fraction, compound ~ **60** 17
fraction, improper ~ **60** 16, 18
fraction, proper ~ **60** 15
fractions, vulgar **60** 15-16
fractocumulus **8** 12
fractostratus **8** 11
frame *Agr. Mach.* **38** 8, 90
frame *Bees* **50** 40
frame, C-shaped ~ **26** 19; **27** 17
frame, heated ~ **28** 16
frame, sectional ~ **38** 56
frame bar **37** 51
frame hive **50** 45-50
frame vent **28** 17
franking machine **22** 24
freeway *Map* **15** 16
freezer **22** 63
freight depot *Map* **15** 91
fresh-air inlet **68** 16
fresh milk filling and packing plant **49** 20
fresh milk tank **49** 15
fresh oil tank **38** 46
freshwater eel **76** 17
freshwater pearl mussel **69** 33
fringe region **7** 34
frog *Agr. Mach.* **38** 8
frog's bit **90** 29
frond **90** 49
frontalis **19** 4
front axle pivot pin **38** 48
front axle suspension **38** 49
front band **44** 9
front, cold ~ **8** 13; **9** 27
front, occluded ~ **9** 25
front, warm ~ **8** 5; **9** 26
front panel, sliding ~ **65** 27
fronts **9** 25-29
fronts, cold ~ **8** 13-17

fronts, warm ~ **8** 5-12
fruit *Alp. Plants etc.* **90** 11, 38, 42
fruit, aggregate ~ *Bot.* **82** 100, 101
fruit, aggregate ~ *Soft Fruit* **31** 28
fruit, compound ~ *Bot.* **82** 100, 101
fruit, compound ~ *Soft Fruit* **31** 28
fruit capsule, mature ~ **94** 44
fruit capsule, ripe ~ **94** 44
fruit cone **84** 2, 29, 30, 36, 41, 57
fruit *Conifers* **84** 53, 64
fruit *Decid. Trees* **83** 4, 19, 28, 45, 69
fruit, dehisced ~ **87** 27
fruit *Flowers etc.* **87** 4, 7, 10, 13, 17, 24, 35, 37, 47; **88** 3, 6, 14
fruit, immature ~ **90** 31
fruit, indehiscent ~ **87** 43
fruit *Industr. Plants* **95** 14, 18, 21, 28, 32, 40, 43, 52, 56, 59
fruiting body **93** 2
fruiting branch *Conifers* **84** 40, 51, 59, 63, 66, 70
fruiting branch *Decid. Trees* **83** 3, 11, 18, 31, 36, 41, 47, 50, 56, 64
fruiting branch *Industr. Plants* **95** 34, 46
fruiting branch *South. Fruits* **96** 38
fruiting branch *Trop. Plants* **94** 2, 37
fruiting palm **96** 2
fruit, mature ~ *Decid. Trees* **83** 61
fruit, mature ~ *Trop. Plants* **94** 33
fruit pests **53** 1-19
fruit picker **29** 22
fruit pip **31** 37, 60
fruit, ripe ~ *Decid. Trees* **83** 61
fruit, ripe ~ *Trop. Plants* **94** 33
fruits **82** 91-102
fruit scale **84** 67
fruits, dehiscent ~ **82** 91-96
fruit *Shrubs etc.* **85** 12, 18, 22, 27, 29, 32; **86** 4, 8, 12 19, 25, 29, 31, 34
fruits, indehiscent ~ **82** 97-102
fruits, Mediterranean ~ **96**
fruit, soft ~ **31** 1-30
fruit *South. Fruits* **96** 19, 26 39, 45
fruits, southern ~ **96**
fruits, subtropical ~ **96**
fruits, tropical ~ **96**
fruit *Trop. Plants* **94** 3, 5, 10, 15, 17, 24, 39
fruit, unripe ~ **90** 31
fruit *Weeds* **34** 11, 20, 23
fruit, young ~ *Decid. Trees* **83** 59
fruit, young ~ *South. Fruits* **96** 31
frustum of a cone **63** 45
fuel tank *Agr. Mach.* **38** 42
fuel tank *Moon L.* **6** 7, 29, 37
fulmar **71** 12
fumigation chamber, mobile ~ **56** 15
fumigation plant, vacuum ~ **56** 11

fumigator, vacuum ~ **56** 11
function, trigonometrical ~ **62** 32
fungi, edible ~ **93**
fungi, esculent ~ **93**
fungi, poisonous ~ **91** 10-13
funnel *Chem.* **66** 16
furrow *Agr.* **36** 8
furrow, gluteal ~ **16** 42
furrow wheel **38** 16
fur seal **79** 18

G

gag *Horse* **44** 53
gag bit **44** 53
gaillardia **33** 19
gaits of the horse **45** 39-44
Galaxy **3** 35
gale **85** 33
galena **67** 14
gallant soldier **34** 31
gall bladder **20** 11, 36
galleries under bark **55** 23-24
gallery *Forest Pests* **55** 24
gall *Forest Pests* **55** 34
gall *Gdn. Pests* **53** 33
gall gnat **53** 40
gall midge **53** 40
gallop, full ~ **45** 43-44, 43, 44
gall wasp **55** 33
galvanometer **11** 44
gamma ray **1** 33, 40
gander **46** 34
gannet **71** 9
gardener **28** 20
garden flowers **33**
garden hoe **39** 1
garden hose **29** 27
garden mould **28** 15
garden pansy **33** 2
garden pests **53**
garden rose **33** 15
garden shovel **28** 14
garden spider **70** 45
garden strawberry **31** 16
garden tiger **77** 7
garden tools **29**
garnet **67** 7
gas, natural ~ **12** 30
gas cap **12** 30
gas circulation unit **56** 16
gas generator **66** 59
gas inlet **66** 2
gas inlet pipe **66** 2
gaskin **45** 36
gasoline canister **57** 36
gas outlet *Chem.* **66** 63
gas pipe *Pest Contr.* **56** 14
gas regulator **66** 6
gas supply **27** 41
gastrocnemius **18** 62
gas tube **56** 35
gas-washing bottle **66** 58
gauge **49** 6
gauze, sterile ~ **22** 58
gauze, wire ~ **66** 18, 19
gearbox *Agr. Mach.* **38** 79
gear-change *Agr. Mach.* **38** 35
gear *Gdn. Tools* **29** 20

gearing *Agr. Mach.* **37** 50, 65
gearing *Overh. Irrign.* **40** 21
gear meter **49** 4
gears *Agr. Mach.* **37** 50, 65
gear shift **38** 23, 35
gears *Overh. Irrign.* **40** 21
gecko **76** 36
Geiger counter **2** 19
Geiger-Müller counter **2** 19
gelding **46** 2
Gemini **3** 28; **4** 55
general practice **22** 1-74
general practitioner **23** 2
geodesy **14** 46-62
geography, physical ~ **11**; **12**; **13**
geology **12** 1-33
geometrid **53** 16; **55** 28
geometry **62; 63**
geometry, elementary ~ **62** 1-58
geometry, Euclidian ~ **62** 1-58
germ **82** 86
German brown trout **76** 15
German pointer **43** 40
German sheepdog **43** 25
German shepherd **43** 25
geyser *Phys. Geog.* **11** 21
Gigantocypris agassizi **81** 1
gill *Dom. Anim.* **46** 24
gill *Edib. Fungi* **93** 4, 6
gill cleft **76** 3
gill cover **76** 5
gill, tufted ~ **76** 19
gill slit **76** 3
gillyflower **33** 7
gipsy moth **53** 1
giraffe **79** 4
giraffe house **68** 10
girth **44** 18, 36
girth, emergency ~ **44** 23
girth, second ~ **44** 23
glacier *Phys. Geog.* **12** 49
glacier snout **12** 51
glacier table **12** 56
gladiolus **33** 11
gland, bulbourethral ~ **20** 75
gland, parotid ~ **19** 9
gland, pituitary ~ **17** 43
gland, prostate ~ **20** 76
gland, submandibular ~ **19** 11
gland, submaxillary ~ **19** 11
gland, suprarenal ~ **20** 29
gland, thyroid ~ **20** 1
glans penis **20** 69
glass case **68** 15
glass sponge **81** 7
glede **74** 11
globe, solar ~ **4** 36
globe, terrestrial ~ **4** 8
globe artichoke **30** 41
glume **41** 11
gluteus maximus **18** 60
gnat **70** 16
Goat *Astron.* **3** 36; **4** 62
goat *Dom. Anim.* **46** 14
goatsbeard *Edib. Fungi* **93** 32
goat's beard *Edib. Fungi* **93** 32
goat's beard *Forest Plants etc.* **89** 5
goatsbeard *Forest Plants etc.* **89** 5
goat willow **83** 24

H

movable-frame hive **50** 45-50
mower, electric ~ **29** 31
mower, hand ~ **29** 34
mower, motor ~ **29** 28
mower, riding ~ **29** 37
mower, rotary ~ **36** 19
mulberry-feeding moth **70** 48
mule *Dom. Anim.* **46** 8
multiplicand **60** 25
multiplication **60** 25
multiplication sign **60** 25
multiplier **60** 25
multiplying **60** 25
multi-tier transport **47** 35
muscle, contractile ~ **50** 17
muscle, deltoid ~ **18** 35
muscle, pectoralis ~ **18** 36
muscles, ocular ~ **19** 44
muscle, sternocleidomastoid ~ **18** 34; **19** 1
muscle, sternomastoid ~ **18** 34; **19** 1
muscle, temporal ~ **19** 3
muscle, thenar ~ **18** 41
muscles of facial expression **19** 6
muscles of the neck **19** 12
muscular system **18** 34-64
musculature **18** 34-64
mushroom **93** 3
mushrooms, poisonous ~ **91** 10-13
musk ox **79** 10
mussel shell **69** 36
mustard *Weeds* **34** 16
mute swan **71** 16
muzzle *Dog* **43** 3, 31
mycelium **41** 4; **93** 2

N

Na atom **1** 8
nacre **69** 34
nadir **4** 13
nail **19** 80
naked boys **91** 3
naked lady **91** 3
nape of the neck **16** 21
narcissus **33** 3
nasicorn **78** 25
navel **16** 34
neck *Horse* **45** 12, 15
neck *Man* **16** 19-21
neck, ground glass ~ **66** 37
neck strap **44** 30
nectary **32** 18
needle *Conifers* **84** 11
needle, hypodermic ~ **22** 65; **24** 54
needle, surgical ~ **22** 57
needle holder **22** 59
nematode **53** 51
Neptune **4** 51
nerve **82** 30
nerve, auditory ~ **17** 64
nerve, femoral ~ **18** 31
nerve, optic ~ *Bees* **50** 23, 24
nerve, optic ~ *Man* **19** 51
nerve, peroneal ~ **18** 33
nerve, radial ~ **18** 28

nerve, sciatic ~ **18** 30
nerve, thoracic ~ **18** 26
nerve, tibial ~ **18** 32
nerve, ulnar ~ **18** 29
nerves **19** 33
nervous system **18** 22-33
nervure *Articulates* **70** 34
nervure *Bot.* **82** 29
nest **71** 28
nesting cavity **71** 29
Net *Astron.* **3** 48
nettle **34** 33
neuropteran **70** 12
neutron **1** 30, 39, 45, 52, 53
neutron bombardment **1** 36, 50
nevé **12** 48
Newfoundland dog **43** 34
New World opossum **78** 2
nightingale **73** 14
Nile crocodile **68** 13
nimbostratus **8** 10
nipple **16** 28
nitrous oxide **26** 3
node **41** 7
node, lymph ~ **19** 10
nodosity **53** 27
North America **14** 12
North Atlantic Drift **14** 30
North Equatorial Current **14** 32
Northern Cross **3** 23
Northern Crown **3** 31
northern gannet **71** 9
northern pike **76** 16
north point **4** 16
North Pole **14** 3
North Sea **14** 26
North Star **3** 1, 34
noseband **44** 7
nose *Dog* **43** 4
nose *Fish etc.* **76** 2
nose *Horse* **45** 6
nose *Man* **16** 10
nostril **45** 7
notch *Forestry* **57** 28
notch *Phys. Geog.* **13** 30
notice **68** 7
nozzle *Moon L.* **6** 3
nozzle *Overh. Irrign.* **40** 33
nozzle *Pest. Contr.* **56** 46
nozzle, pistol-type ~ **56** 28
nozzle, revolving ~ **29** 44
nucleus **1** 43
nucleus, atomic ~ **1** 2, 16, 29, 35, 49, 51
number, abstract ~ **60** 3
number, cardinal ~ **60** 5
number, complex ~ **60** 14
number, concrete ~ **60** 4
number, even ~ **60** 11
number, four-figure ~ **60** 3
number, mixed ~ **60** 10
number, negative ~ **60** 8
number, odd ~ **60** 12
number, ordinal ~ **60** 6
number, positive ~ **60** 7
number, prime ~ **60** 13
number, whole ~ **60** 10, 18
numbers **60** 1-22
numeral, Arabic ~ **60** 2
numeral, Roman ~ **60** 1

numerator **60** 15
nun moth **55** 17
nursery gardener **28** 20
nursery hand **28** 45, 46
nursery sapling **56** 15
nutation **4** 24
nut *Bot.* **82** 98
nut *Industr. Plants* **95** 44
nut *South. Fruits* **96** 60
nutcracker **73** 1
nuthatch **73** 11
nutmeg **94** 34, 35
nutmeg tree **94** 30
nuts **32** 59, 37-51

O

oak apple **55** 34
oak gall **55** 34
oak-gall wasp **55** 33
oak tree **83** 1
oat-grass **42** 22
oat panicle **41** 27
oats **41** 1
oblique, external ~ **18** 43
obliquus externus abdominis **18** 43
observation opening **5** 13
observation port *Agr. Mach.* **37** 27
observation room **5** 33
observation shaft **5** 30
observation telescope **67** 31
observation window **25** 8
observatory **5** 1-16; **9** 7
observatory, solar ~ **5** 29-33
observatory dome **5** 12
occipitalis **18** 50; **19** 2
occipitofrontalis **19** 4
occiput **16** 2
occlusion **9** 25
ocean *Map* **14** 19-26
ocean *Phys. Geog.* **13** 26
ocean current, cold ~ **14** 27
ocean current, warm ~ **14** 28
ocean currents **14** 30-45
ocean drifts **14** 30-45
ocean station vessel **9** 7
ocellus *Bees* **50** 2
ocellus *Dom. Anim.* **46** 32
octagon **67** 17
octahedron **67** 6, 14, 16
Octans **3** 43
Octant **3** 43
odd-pinnate **82** 42
oesophagus *Bees* **50** 19
oesophagus *Man* **17** 49; **20** 23, 40
office, physician's ~ **22** 1-74
offshoot **82** 21
off switch **10** 15
oil, crude ~ *Phys. Geog.* **12** 31
oil, viscous ~ **57** 35
oil bath air cleaner *Agr. Mach.* **38**J 54
oil bath air filter *Agr. Mach.* **38** 54
oil palm **95** 54
oil reservoir **37** 29, 93
oil sump *Agr. Mach.* **38** 45

pod, unripe ~ **86** 22
pod corn **41** 31
poet's daffodil **33** 4
poet's narcissus **33** 4
point, angular ~ **62** 1
point, diamond ~ **24** 40
point, equinoctial ~ **3** 6, 7
pointer *Chem.* **65** 34
pointer *Dog* **43** 40, 43
pointer *Hosp.* **26** 28
point *Maths.* **62** 1-23
point of Aries **3** 6
point of contact **62** 49
point of inflexion **63** 21
point of intersection **62** 1
points, equinoctial ~ **3** 6-7
points of the horse **45** 1-38
poison gland **50** 14
poison sac **50** 13
polar bear **80** 11
Polaris **3** 1, 34
polar wind zone **9** 51
pole *Horse* **44** 21
pole, celestial ~ **3** 1; **4** 24, 26
pole, geographical ~ **14** 3
pole, hooked ~ **50** 55
pole chain **44** 20
pole, terrestrial ~ **14** 3
Pole Star **3** 1, 34
polhode **4** 28
Politzer bag **22** 37
polje **13** 72
pollen **50** 3, 35; **82** 65
pollen basket **50** 6
pollen comb **50** 7
pollen sac **84** 45, 50
pollen tube **82** 66
pollex **19** 64
polyanthus narcissus **33** 4
Polycheles **81** 15
polygon **62** 40
polygon, eight-sided ~ **67** 17
polygon, five-sided ~ **67** 9
polygon, regular ~ **62** 41
polygon, six-sided ~ **67** 15
polyhedron, eight-faced ~ **67** 6
polyhedron, forty-eight faced ~
   67 13
polyhedron, four-faced ~ **67** 1
polyhedron, regular ~ **67** 11
polyhedron, six-faced ~ **67** 2
polyhedron, twenty-faced ~ **67**
   11
polyhedron, twenty-four faced ~
   67 12
polyp, hydroid ~ **81** 9
polypod **89** 16
polypody **89** 16
pome **82** 102
pomegranate **96** 16
Pomeranian **43** 20
pomes **31**
pommel horn **44** 38
pompon dahlia **33** 23
pond *Map* **15** 79
pons **17** 46
pons cerebelli **17** 46
pons cerebri **17** 46
pontic, porcelain ~ **24** 29
pontoon bridge **15** 46

pony **48** 4
poodle **43** 36
poor man's weatherglass **34** 27
popcorn **41** 31
poplar **83** 15
poppy flower **34** 4
poppy **34** 2
poppy seed **34** 5
porcupine **78** 13
porifer **69** 13
post crown **24** 31
post *Dent.* **24** 34
post *Forestry* **57** 17; **58** 30, 47
post *Wine Grow.* **51** 7
potato **41** 38, 40
potato, Irish ~ **41** 38
potato, kidney-shaped ~ **41** 38
potato, long ~ **41** 38
potato, pear-shaped ~ **41** 38
potato, purple ~ **41** 38
potato, red ~ **41** 38
potato, round ~ **41** 38
potato, round-oval ~ **41** 38
potato, white ~ **41** 38
potato, yellow ~ **41** 38
potato apple **41** 43
potato basket **39** 25
potato beetle **53** 52
potato berry **41** 43
potato, flat-oval ~ **41** 38
potato fork **39** 5
potato harvester **37** 59-84
potato haulm **41** 41
potato hoe **39** 24
potato hook **39** 6
potato plant **41** 38
potato planter **39** 21
potato rake **39** 20
potato top **41** 41
potato tuber **41** 40
pot plant **28** 25
potting bench **28** 12
potting table **28** 12
pouch, gular ~ **71** 8
poultry **46** 19-36
poultry farming **47** 1-27
poultry keeping **47**
poultry management, intensive ~
   47 1-27
power **61** 1
power lift **38** 24-29
power saw *Forestry* **57** 22, 27; **58**
   13
power take-off **36** 21; **37** 49
power take-off clutch **38** 40
power take-off gear **38** 38
power take-off gear-change **38**
   23, 40
power take-off shaft **36** 21; **37** 49
power unit **57** 34
precession **4** 24
precipitation **8** 18
precipitation, scattered ~ **8** 19
precipitation, types of ~ **8** 18-19
precipitation area **9** 30
precipitation gauge **10** 44
premolar **19** 18
preparation and sterilization
   room **26** 34-54
preparation level **37** 16

preparation room **26** 34-54
prepuce **20** 70
prescription **22** 3, 20
presorting **37** 82
press roller **37** 64
pressure, atmospheric ~ **9** 4
pressure, barometric ~ **9** 4
pressure chamber **56** 44
pressure gauge *Hosp.* **25** 53; **26** 29
pressure gauge *Overh. Irrign.* **40**
   10
pressure gauge *Pest Contr.* **56** 42
pressure indicator **25** 55
pressure pipe *Market Gdn.* **28** 8
pressure point **21** 14
pressure trace **25** 57
pressure transducer **27** 32
primates **80** 12-16
prime focus cage **5** 2
Prime meridian **14** 5
principal **61** 7
prism, hexagonal ~ **67** 21
prism, monoclinic ~ **67** 24
prism, quadratic ~ **63** 34
prism, triangular ~ **63** 37
privet **85** 6
privet hawkmoth **70** 55
probe, bulb-headed ~ **22** 53; **26**
   40
probe *Dent.* **24** 46
probe, hollow ~ **26** 41
probe, olive-pointed ~ **22** 53; **26**
   40
proboscidean **78** 20
proboscidian **78** 20
proboscis *Articulates* **70** 17, 56
proboscis *Mammals* **78** 21
procaviid **78** 24
processionary moth **55** 14
proctoscope **23** 17, 19, 21
proctoscopy **23** 18
Procyon **3** 15
product **60** 25
profit **61** 7
program selector switch **25** 50
projection, conical ~ **14** 8
projection, cylindrical ~ **14** 9
projection booth **5** 27
projection dome **5** 21
projector **5** 23
prominence, solar ~ **4** 40
prong *Agr. Impl.* **39** 4
propeller mixer **52** 6
proportion, simple ~ **61** 8-10
prostate **20** 76
prothorax **55** 4; **70** 29
proton **1** 2, 16, 31
protoplasm **69** 3
protoprism **67** 19, 20
protopyramid **67** 19, 20
protozoans **69** 1-12
protrusion, massive ~ **11** 29
protuberance, frontal ~ **16** 4
pruner **29** 11
pruningknife **29** 9
pruning saw **29** 16
pruning shears **29** 50
prussic acid **56** 15
pseudocarp **31** 21; **96** 12, 62
pseudopod **69** 4

remains **15** 72
rendezvous radar antenna **6** 42
reniform **82** 38
rennet vat **49** 48
reptile enclosure **68** 12
reptiles **76** 27-41
requin **76** 1
rescue **21** 18-23, 28-33, 34-38
rescuer **21** 29, 34
research microscope, binocular ~ **23** 51
research rocket **7** 24
reservoir rock **12** 29
residential area **15** 28
respiration, artificial ~ **21** 24-27
respirator **21** 27; **26** 25
respiratory apparatus **21** 27; **26** 24
respiratory functions **23** 31
respiratory machine **26** 1
respiratory rate **23** 27
resuscitation **21** 24-27
resuscitation, mouth-to-mouth ~ **21** 26
resuscitation, mouth-to-nose ~ **21** 26
resuscitation apparatus **21** 27
resuscitator **21** 27
Reticulum **3** 48
retina **19** 49
retort **65** 13
retort ring **66** 15
return tap **66** 49
reversing gear **38** 41
revolving die hammer **58** 12
rhesus macaque **80** 12
rhesus monkey **80** 12
rhinoceros **78** 25
Rhiptoglossa **76** 33
rhizome **31** 18
rhizopod **69** 1
rhomb **62** 35
rhombic crystal system **67** 23
rhombohedron **67** 22
rhomboid **62** 36
rhombus **62** 35
rhynchophore **70** 4
rib *Bot.* **82** 29
Ribes **31** 1-15
ribgrass **92** 11
ribs, false ~ **17** 10
ribs, true ~ **17** 9
ribwort **92** 11
ribwort plantain **92** 11
rice *Arable Crops* **41** 1; **41** 29
rice grain **41** 30
rickstand **36** 28, 29
riddle **28** 13
ride *Forestry* **57** 1
ride *Map* **15** 112
rider *Chem.* **65** 33
rider bar **65** 31
rider holder **65** 32
ridge *Phys. Geog.* **12** 36; **13** 60
ridge *Roof* **121** 2
ridge vent **28** 11
ridging hoe **29** 5
Rigel **3** 13
right angle **62** 9, 32
rind **82** 8
ring, annual ~ **57** 24

ring *Chem.* **66** 15
ringed snake **76** 38
ring *Forestry* **58** 4
ring *Maths.* **62** 57
ring finger **19** 67
ringsnake **76** 38
ripple marks **13** 41
river arm **13** 2
riverbed **13** 68
river *Map* **15** 76
river *Phys. Geog.* **13** 61
river, navigable ~ **15** 45
river, subterranean ~ **13** 83
river bend **13** 11
river branch **13** 2
river mouth **13** 1
river terrace **13** 49, 63
river valley **13** 57-70
riving hammer **58** 5
rivulet *Map* **15** 80
rivulet *Phys. Geog.* **13** 8
road bridge **15** 55
road, good ~ **15** 30
road, main ~ **15** 83
road, metalled ~ **15** 30
road, poor ~ **15** 99
road, secondary ~ **15** 36
road, unmetalled ~ **15** 99
road over railway **15** 22
robin **73** 15
robin redbreast **73** 15
rock **13** 25; **68** 2
rocket engine **6** 3
rock, impermeable ~ **12** 23, **13** 78
rock, impervious ~ **12** 23; **13** 78
rock, piece of ~ **6** 15
rock, sedimentary ~ **12** 1; **13** 48
rock, stratified ~ **13** 48
rock face *Phys. Geog.* **12** 43; **13** 28
rock goat **79** 7
rock island **13** 12
rock rose **89** 20
rock salt **67** 2
rockslide **11** 46
rock slip **11** 46
rock terrace **13** 47
rodents **78** 12-19
roller *Birds* **71** 25; **72** 6
roller, rubber-disc ~ **37** 82
roll *Horse* **44** 48
roof, glass ~ **28** 5
rook *Birds* **73** 2
rooster **35** 37; **46** 21
root *Arable Crops* **41** 17, 45
root *Bot.* **82** 16-18
root *Horse* **45** 34
root *Industr. Plants* **95** 43
root *Man* **19** 36
root *Maths.* **63** 12
root, adventitious ~ **82** 78, 81
root, aerial ~ **82** 80
root, primary ~ **82** 16
root, secondary ~ **82** 17
root, tuberous ~ **82** 79
root crops **41** 38-45
root gall **53** 27
root hair **41** 18; **82** 18
root louse **53** 26
roots **82** 78-82

root thorn **82** 81
rope *First Aid* **21** 30
ropeway, aerial ~ **15** 67
rosebay **85** 13
rosebud **33** 16
rose, double ~ **33** 17
rose-ear **43** 2
rose hip **82** 100
rose laurel **85** 13
rose *Market Gdn.* **28** 28
rose thorn **33** 18
rotation axis **67** 4
round worm **54** 31
rowan **83** 42
royal fern **89** 16
royal osmund **89** 16
royal water lily **90** 17
rubber belt, studded ~ **37** 79
rubber plant **95** 33
rubber tree **95** 33
rubble **11** 47
rule of three sum **61** 8-10
ruminant **46** 1
ruminants **78** 28-30; **79** 1-10
rump *Horse* **45** 31
runch **34** 18
runner bean **30** 8
runner *Soft Fruit* **31** 20
running wheel **37** 41,56
rush *Phys. Geog.* **13** 17
Russula vesca **93** 23
rye **41** 1,2
ryegrass, perennial ~ **42** 26

S

sable *Mammals* **79** 15
sacrum **17** 21; **20** 59
saddle *Phys. Geog.* **12** 16, 42
saddle, English ~ **44** 45-49
saddle-pad **44** 17, 31
saddle seat **44** 37
saddle tree **86** 1
saddle, western ~ **44** 37-44
saddles **44** 37-49
safety bonnet **58** 36
safety brake **58** 15
safety catch *Atom* **2** 40
safety helmet **57** 23
safety hood **58** 36
saffron milk cap **93** 29
Sagittarius **3** 37; **4** 61
sagittate **82** 37
sago palm **95** 58
sainfoin **42** 10
salad chicory **30** 40
salad plants **30** 36-40
salamander **76** 22
salamanders **76** 20-22
salientians **76** 23-26
salina *Map* **15** 32
sallow **83** 24
salt, common ~ **1** 9
salt works *Map* **15** 32
sandhills **15** 6
sand lizard **76** 27
sand *Map* **15** 6
sand star **81** 11
San-José scale **53** 35

T